# Scott McC[...]

# ZOT!

KITCHEN SINK PRESS

NORTHAMPTON, MASSACHUSETTS

publisher
DENIS KITCHEN

reprint editors
PHILIP AMARA &
CATHERINE GARNIER

designers
DOUGLAS BANTZ AND LISA STONE

art director
AMIE BROCKWAY

senior vp, production
JIM KITCHEN

executive vp
SCOTT HYMAN

chief financial officer
COREY SCHWARTZ

senior director, sales and marketing
JAMIE RIEHLE

director of legal affairs
DOROTHY VARON

national sales director
ERIC HYMAN

customer service manager
KAREN LOWMAN

managing editor
JOHN WILLS

promotions designer
C. EVAN METCALF

warehouse manager
VIC LISEWSKI

Written and Drawn by
# SCOTT McCLOUD

Painted Colors by
**DENIS McFARLING**

Lettered by
**BOB LAPPAN**
with
**TODD KLEIN (part 1)**
**CARRIE McCARTHY SPIEGLE (parts 2 & 3)**

Consulting Editors
**KURT BUSIEK & ADAM PHILIPS**

Original Series Editors and Publishers
**CATHERINE YRONWODE & DEAN MULLANEY**

Thanks to Adobe Systems and Strata Inc. for Photoshop, Illustrator, and Vision3D, used
sparingly in this project, but quite indispensable for the next one (keep your eyes peeled).

Special Thanks to Kurt Busiek, cat yronwode, Dean Mullaney, Denis Kitchen, Bob Lappan, To[n]
Ziuko, Adam Philips, Richard Howell; Bob, Bob, Joey, Ernie and all the folks at DC; Patro[n]
Saints Will Eisner and Art Spiegelman; Special Medal of Honor to the long-suffering Den[is]
McFarling who had to color some of these pages as many as three times over the years; forev[er]
in debt to Carol Kalish and Professor Larry Bakke, both sorely missed; and, of course, to Mo[m]
(Hi, Mom!)

The stories in this book were and are dedicated to my father, whose untimely death great[ly]
influenced my decision to leave my day job and create my own series. I'd like to further dedica[te]
this and all my work to Ivy, my wife of eight years and our daughters, Sky and Winter. He[re]
in cold print, sadly, the only space they'll ever share with him.

# *foreword*

The first issue of my first comic book *Zot!* hit the stands in the Spring of 1984. The symbolism of that timing has lost some of its punch over the years. In retrospect, 1984 conjures up images of Reagan and MTV and maybe the first Macintosh computers. But for the four decades preceding its arrival, thanks to George Orwell's relentlessly grim novel of the same name, 1984 had become synonymous with doom and despair and with all our fears for the future of mankind. Spring, on the other hand, carried the opposite connotation: a time for rebirth, renewal and hope. The notion that 1984 should even *have* a Spring seemed almost in bad taste, like throwing a party to announce that you have cancer. But Spring arrived, just the same, and *Zot!* with it.

I was twenty-three years old that Spring and working to have hope for the future, even though I had convinced myself that the human race would probably annihilate itself before I ever reached thirty. The way I saw it, though—still see it—is that if you think there's a ninety percent chance of disaster, then the only rational response is to concentrate that much harder on the remaining ten. Zot!'s world was built around that hopeful ten percent, and around all the ten percent futures we've discarded over the years. This idea would lead me, again and again, throughout the series, back to the dual themes of hope and disillusionment, utopias and dystopias, Spring and 1984.

*Zot!* ran for thirty-six issues through 1991. During *Zot!*'s early run, a handful of talented writers and artists working on other books turned their attention to the darker side of the superhero, and produced a grimmer grittier world-view which (in lesser hands) quickly became the default style for American mainstream comics. By comparison, *Zot!* looked, and still looks, very innocent and sunny, exuding an almost painfully naïve hopefulness, but the dark side is there for those who want to dig a little deeper.

This first collection, the color issues, are especially childlike and awkward, but then, so was I. It had been an obsessive dream of mine to make comics since I was fourteen years old. Nine years later I was getting my chance for the first time, so the twenty-three-year-old me and the fourteen-year-old me and all the me's in between whipped out our pens and began to make up for lost time. Some of the results can embarrass me to this day, but on balance I'm pretty happy with the thing. I look at it now, eleven years later, and I see the inventiveness and the enthusiasm and the innocence that led to its creation.

And the hope.

And 1984.

# W

hen we started out, I was going to be the writer and Scott was going to be the artist.

I met Scott McCloud on the first day of seventh grade, at the William Diamond Junior High School in Lexington, Massachusetts. Neither of us were interested in comics at the time—I was into science fiction and model rocketry and fighter jets, I think, and Scott seemed to spend much of his time drawing elaborate blueprints for large spaceships, carefully designing crew quarters with individual bathrooms, adequate corridor space and stuff like that. We didn't have a whole lot in common beyond that I became friends with someone Scott had been friends with in elementary school, and we didn't have any classes together, but nonetheless we struck up an acquaintance, which became a friendship based on an odd sort of barter system. Scott had a pool table and liked to play chess. I wanted to get out of the house, I liked to play pool, and I was an adequate chess player (by fairly limited standards—I could beat my Dad and my sisters). So for every game of chess I'd play with Scott, he'd play a game of pool with me.

In fairly short order, Scott was regularly beating me at chess, unless I managed to distract him with comedy to the point where he didn't think through his moves. And he was regularly beating me at pool, too, since I never gained the habit of thinking through my shots. But that's neither here nor there, is it?

Along the way, I got into the habit of collecting comics, and a couple of years into our friendship I pressed on Scott a run of the original *X-Men*—the Lee/Kirby/Thomas/Roth

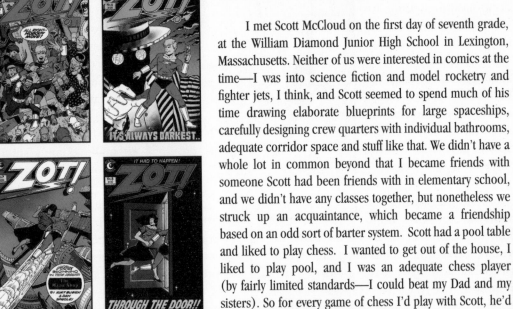

# ORIGINS

## Introduction
## by Kurt
## Busiek

era. Reluctantly, he read them, and got enthusiastic about the form more or less against his will. I loaned him more comics. He never did become much of a collector (for the historical record, the first comic Scott paid his own money for was *Warlock* #9, by Jim Starlin), but we both got interested in creating our own comics. We created our own superheroes—a team called "The Phenomenals," to start—and started keeping elaborate notebooks full of character concepts and plots, and doing drawings of our characters and of the Marvel Comics heroes and villains.

I don't remember exactly how we decided to write and draw a comic ourselves, but when we did, since Scott was clearly the better artist and since I'd had writing ambitions since I first tried to write my own Oz novel back when I was four or five, we decided that we'd come up with a story together, and that, as noted above, I'd write it, and that Scott would draw it.

The result was *The Battle of Lexington*, a sixty-page battle-fest pitting five Marvel characters against five other Marvel characters for no apparent reason, set at our high school and demolishing the place. It took us three years to finish it—or, more accurately, to give up on it and truncate the plot we'd originally assumed would take about fifteen pages to tell. Along the way, the heroes spilled out

from our high school and destroyed much of the Lexington Battle Green, the town library and even the Friendly's restaurant we'd stop in at a lot for french fries and burgers. Also along the way, we started to figure out how to go about the comic book thing, how to present a story visually, how to use dialogue to establish the characters and move the story along, how to pace a story from panel to panel, and so on. We argued a lot, as we figured things out. And we both decided that creating comic books was something we'd like to do professionally, and started thinking about actual careers in the business. Naturally, we'd be a team. I'd be the writer, and Scott would be the artist.

We did more than just *The Battle of Lexington*, of course. We did an actual, approved Marvel/DC crossover called (*ahem*) *Pow! Biff! Pops!,* as part of the season opening of the Boston Pops Orchestra one year. Their opening night theme was "comic heroes night," and they did the Neal Hefti *Batman* theme, the "Flight of the Bumblebee" (better known as the theme to the

*Green Hornet*) and others. And as a benefit, I wrote and Scott laid out a comic book teaming up Superman, Batman, Robin, Wonder Woman, Spider-Man, Captain America, the Sub-Mariner and the Human Torch, as they rescued the kidnapped Pops orchestra from an evil mastermind. The finished art was done by our friend Christopher Bing, whose mother was on the Pops Committee and had put the whole thing together, and the lettering was by Richard Howell, currently the editor at Claypool Comics and the writer/artist of *Deadbeats*. We had full approval from both DC and Marvel to do this, the comics were sold at opening night as a fund-raiser (only 250 were produced and any not sold that night were destroyed as part of the deal with Marvel and DC, so if you want to find a copy, good luck), and we got to meet Sol Harrison at the opening night banquet.

We also did a story called "Once More . . . With Feeling," which we intended to sell to *Heavy Metal* or *Epic Illustrated*, despite the fact that it was drawn on typing paper and inked with a Pilot Razor Point. It's notable among our collaborations for being the only one in which I penciled the lettering and Scott inked it, Scott having gotten sick of doing all the drudge work.

Scott also encouraged me to draw my own comics (as, indeed, he continues to do to this day), and I got a few pages into a couple before abandoning them, while he wrote and sketched out what he called a "layout comic," *Out Of The Frying Pan, Into The Fire*, starring the Neal Adams-era X-Men. Resisting drudge work? Writing his own stuff? I should have seen the handwriting on the wall, but I didn't.

We both went to the same college—Syracuse University, in upstate New York—where Scott enrolled in the illustration program, and I took as many courses as I could that I thought would help me become a comic book writer. And we continued to argue, to experiment with our craft, and to collaborate.

Our friend Richard Howell, whom I mentioned above, had become the co-editor, along with Carol Kalish, at New Media Publishing, and they asked Scott and me to do a project for a planned (but never, as it turned out, published) comics series showcasing new talent. So we created a new group of superheroes, Vanguard—and in what was becoming a traditional move for us, they were set at our college. And sure enough, during their big fights with villains, they were going to destroy a lot of it. Anyway, we had a lot of fun, created a bunch of characters we still feel fond of today, worked out a four-part story, and I think three issues were written, two penciled and one inked by the time the project was canceled. And for the same never-to-exist magazine, we did Challenger, another new character, in a ten-or-twelve page story that I scripted and Scott laid out.

But *Challenger* was a change for us. A change I didn't see at the time, but in retrospect, it's easy to see. Everything we'd worked on together up until then was ours—we created it, worked it out, and saw it through together. But *Challenger* was mine. I wrote the story mostly on my own. I did the preliminary design sketch Scott worked from. Scott may have been the artist, but *Challenger* felt different from our earlier collaborations. *Challenger*—the story of the son of the world's greatest superhero, taking on the name and costume himself—was creatively my baby, but mostly just a craft exercise for Scott. We were heading off in different directions.

And Scott was working on this new idea, the fruits of which you hold in your hands. Something of his own—that he'd write and draw himself.

At this point, let me spend a little time on how Scott works. Scott is perhaps the ideal expression of the homily "Catch me a fish and I eat for a day; teach me to fish and I eat for a lifetime." Scott's not terribly interested in people doing things for him. He'd rather have them show him how to do it himself. He doesn't just want it done, he wants to know how it works and why it works and what's going on underneath. He wants to *understand* the process, whatever it is. When we did *The Battle of Lexington,* Scott experimented with wild layouts, bizarre panel arrangements, loopy three-dimensional graphics—and most of it turned out to be little more than a hard-to-read mess. By the end of the story, Scott was doing very straightforward, very bold, very clear storytelling . . . not because it was simple, but because it *worked.* Because he'd tried enough things to get his mind into the process and figure out enough of what makes it tick so that he was able to make a conscious choice toward simplicity. When we did *Challenger,* I handed Scott a script with one splash page and nine or more pages that were all six-panel pages. Scott spent a week drawing grids, working out all the possible combinations of panels that would result in six roughly same-size panels on a single page, and then looked over all his sketched-out pages to figure out which panel arrangements were clear, which were confusing, which were dramatic, which were useful . . . he took the process apart to see how it worked, so he'd know what he was doing when he did the actual job. It's the way his mind works; he doesn't take things on faith, he has to understand. He has to learn.

That's why I should have known from the start that what I said at the beginning of this introduction was never true. We were never on that track, aiming toward me being the writer and Scott being the artist. We may have thought we were, but that's just because we hadn't figured out how to describe what was really going on yet. What we were doing was figuring out our craft, figuring out how to do what it was that attracted us to comics. In my case, that was writing, and over the course of those years, I learned enough about conceiving, structuring and crafting stories so that I got work at DC and Marvel with little trouble. But what Scott was learning wasn't how to draw comics, it was how to *make* comics—writing *and* drawing. We

were teaching each other to fish, as we learned how to do it ourselves, but we were learning different kinds of fishing.

So we got out of college, and I did become the writer, working on various projects with various artists. And Scott went to work for DC's production department, where he further delved into the process of making comics *work,* demystifying the magic by which lines on paper turn into printed magazines.

And then he did *Zot!*

It's not that simple, of course. Scott had been working on *Zot!* for quite a while before the comic became a reality, and I had input into it, here and there, two bits of which I'll mention here:

First, the name. When Scott was first messing around with the idea of a young space-hero, he was coming up with names like Comet Calloway, Doppler Dan and Starr Barton—and for a time, when the guy was planned to be a robot, he was called 'Bot. And in some letter column somewhere, a reader asked Scott if Zot was named for the lightning-bolt sound effect in the *B.C.* comic strip, and Scott said no, he wasn't. Well, let me set the record straight. I named the guy, and I got the name directly from that lightning-bolt sound effect in *B.C.* The truth shall out.

Second, the first issue. I wrote a little bit of the first issue—not much, maybe six or seven word balloons, max. I was helping Scott as a "script consultant," going over his rough scripts and suggesting ways he could make the exposition read more smoothly, or make scene transitions work better, that sort of thing. And he was having some trouble with the dialogue in some spots, so I wrote some alternate word balloons to show him how I thought it should go, and he ended up using a few of them.

And he never needed me to do it again.

This is what I mean by the "teaching to fish" analogy. When I couldn't explain to Scott how to make a scene work, I showed him how to do it, and he didn't just see the surface—he saw the process. He understood *why* I was recommending those changes, and once he knew the *why* of it, he could do it for himself.

And on he went, looking for the next part of the process he could figure out.

One last thing, and then I'm out of here: At the 1994 Dallas Fantasy Fair, one of the high points of the Harvey Awards ceremony was seeing Scott win the Best Writer award for *Understanding Comics*. In his acceptance speech, Scott very graciously said that he felt the award should go to me (I was also nominated, as it happens), since I'd been the one to teach him to write.

Well, thanks, Scott, but no.

We taught each other to write, starting off with me slouched in that old green chair by the radiator, while you sat at the drawing board on your desk and we faced the task of getting a bunch of characters on stage, introducing them, and making them interact in such a way that it would make sense to a reader. I may have written the words that went on the pages, but making the story

work was something we stumbled through together, wandering down blind alleys and falling into pits of our own devising before we started to get a sense of how it might work, of how we might get what we saw in our brains actually onto the page. You taught yourself to write as surely as anything I did, and I learned as much from you as I did from my own efforts.

And maybe some day we'll finally collaborate on something that actually gets published and seen. But if and when we do, it won't be with me as the writer and you as the artist. It'll be the way we did things all along—we'll be writing it together. I may be the one who types the words, and you may be the one who blocks out the visuals, but if the story and the ideas within it don't come from both of us, then it couldn't possibly be like the old days.

And without that, what's the point?

What follows is Scott's first public foray into telling his own stories through the comics medium. If you've read 'em before, you know how good they are. If you haven't, you're about to meet some unforgettable characters and experience some engaging, dramatic and heartfelt adventures. I hope you have as good a time with them as I did seeing them emerge from the pencil and the imagination of that quiet kid who sat at the corner of the table in that seventh grade lunchroom . . .

— Kurt Busiek, February 1996

I'M GONNA *MISS* L.A....

I'M GONNA MISS *DALE* AND *CHRIS* AND THE KIDS ON THE BEACH.

HECK, I'LL EVEN MISS *MYRON LEFKOWITZ*--I'M NOT PICKY...

I JUST WISH MY FOLKS COULD GET *STUCK* ON PLACES THE WAY I DO.

ANN ARBOR.... LEXINGTON... SPRINGFIELD.... NOW L.A. .... JUST WHEN I'M GETTING TO FEEL AT HOME--*BOOM!* "PACK YOUR THINGS, JENNY, WE'RE MOVING AGAIN."

I MAY BE ONLY 13, BUT I FEEL *80!* I'VE BEEN SO MANY PLACES--

--AND IT'S ALL JUST A *DEAD END!*

I JUST WANT TO *DO* SOMETHING BEFORE I DIE OF--

?

WELL, HEL-*LO* THERE!

WHAT ARE *YOU* DOING IN A PLACE LIKE THIS? I THOUGHT THERE WASN'T A POND FOR *MILES!*

HEY DON'T RUN OFF, *FROGGIE!* I JUST WANT TO *TALK!*

YOU LOOK LOST. MAYBE I CAN *HELP...*

...'CAUSE I KNOW HOW IT FEELS...

HEY, SHRIMP!

HI, BUTCH.

WHAT'CHA DOIN', SIS? PLAYIN' *"GAWD-I'M-DEPRESSED"* AGAIN?

OH, LEAVE ME ALONE, BUTCH.

*UH-HUH.* I *THOUGHT* SO.

EY, WHAT'S THIS?
GOT A NEW
OYFRIEND?

HE'S A BIG ONE!
GIVE HIM HERE!

NO WAY!
NOT AFTER
WHAT YOU
DID TO THE
LAST ONE!

AW, C'MON!

NO!!

GIVE 'IM
BACK!

URDERER!
OME BACK
HERE!

HA! HA! HA!

BUTCH, PLEASE!
ST--OOOMPH!

HA! HA!
HA! HA!

CHUMPH!

THE LAST STRAW.

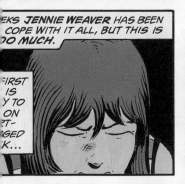

EKS JENNIE WEAVER HAS BEEN
COPE WITH IT ALL, BUT THIS IS
DO MUCH.

FIRST
Y TO
ON
RT-
GED
K...

...BUT IT HOLDS ITS PLACE AS A
SOFT AND EERIE GLOW
CATCHES HER EYE.

A GLOW FROM
SOMETHING...

OUT OF THIS WORLD.

WHAT...

...IS IT?

IT'S,...LIKE A WINDOW...
BUT TO WHERE??

ARE THOSE
BUILDINGS??

AND THERE'S
SOMETHING
MOVING...

...COMING
THIS WAY...

3

YAAAAA!!

¡RAHRR!!

TOO LATE! SHE'LL BE TRAMPLED NOW, UNLESS--

AND WITHOUT A MOMENT'S PAUSE--

HOLD ON! I'LL SAVE YOU!

≥AK!≤

IT'S NOT *YOU* THEY'RE AFTER!

THEY AREN'T EVEN PROGRAMMED TO *NOTICE* YOU!

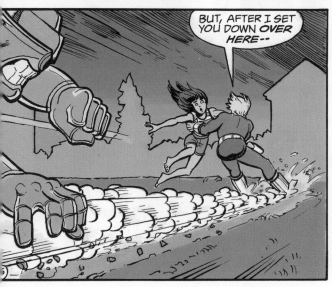

BUT, AFTER I SET YOU DOWN *OVER HERE*--

--I'LL MAKE 'EM NOTICE ME!

OUT FLASHES A GLEAMING GOLDEN PISTOL, AND--

YOU ALL RIGHT, MISS? SORRY TO WHIP YOU AROUND LIKE THAT.

IT'S JUST THAT-- WELL, THEY'RE *BIG SUCKERS*, Y'KNOW? HAD TO GET YOU OUT OF THE WAY *QUICKLY*.

HMM, ONLY *ONE CHARGE* LEFT. GOOD THING THERE WEREN'T *MORE* OF THEM.

I REALLY OUGHT TO GET A *BETTER MODEL*, BUT SOMEHOW I CAN'T PART WITH THIS OLD *10-SHOOTER*.

HEY, SORRY ABOUT THIS MESS.

I...*um*...IS SOMETHING *WRONG*?

WHO *ARE* YOU??

OH, PARDON ME... *ZACHARY T. PALEOZOGT,* AT YOUR SERVICE. BUT YOU CAN CALL ME *ZOT!*

*NOW...NOT THAT IT ISN'T APPEALING--*

--BUT, YOU'VE STILL GOT THAT *CONFUSED LOOK* ON YOUR FACE...

OH, SORRY...

NO *WAIT,* I'M *STILL CONFUSED!* I MEAN, LIKE... WHAT'S THE *BIG GLOWING THING?*

OH, THAT'S WHAT WE CALL A *SPATIO-DIMEN--* OR, UH... NO...A *TEMPORAL DISPL--* NO THAT WASN'T IT...

WELL, IT'S KIND OF A *WINDOW TO ANOTHER WORLD.*

YOU'RE... FROM ANOTHER WORLD...

THAT'S RIGHT.

UH.... ANY ONE IN *PARTICULAR?*

WELL, THAT'S A LITTLE HARDER TO EXPLAIN. LET'S JUST SAY *"ELSEWHERE".*

NEXT QUESTION?

WELL, IF IT'S NOT TOO MUCH *TROUBLE--* I'D LIKE TO KNOW ABOUT THE *BIG METAL THINGS.* WHY THEY'RE HERE--

--WHY *YOU'RE* HERE.

I DON'T MEAN TO *PRY...*

NO IT'S ALL RIGHT. Hmm...

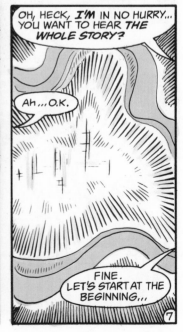

OH, HECK, *I'M* IN NO HURRY... YOU WANT TO HEAR *THE WHOLE STORY?*

Ah...O.K.

FINE. LET'S START AT THE BEGINNING...

7

"ACCORDING TO THIS **LEGEND** OF THEIRS, THE KEY COULD OPEN THE FAMOUS "**DOORWAY AT THE EDGE OF THE UNIVERSE**" --THIS OLD-FASHIONED DOOR JUST HANGING OUT IN THE **MIDDLE OF NOWHERE** THAT NO ONE'S BEEN ABLE TO MOVE, OPEN OR EVEN DAMAGE FOR **MILLIONS OF YEARS**!

"BIG TOURIST ATTRACTION...

"ANYWAY, ONE DAY THIS GUY ACTUALLY MANAGES TO **STEAL** THE KEY RIGHT FROM UNDER THEIR NOSES! THE CHURCH IS **FURIOUS**! THEY SEND OUT **WARSHIPS** JUST TO GET THIS GUY!

"THEY TEAR UP A LOT OF GROUND ON A LOT OF WORLDS AND GET A LOT OF PEOPLE **MAD** IN THE PROCESS."

"MY PEOPLE INCLUDED.

"WELL THEY FINALLY **CATCH** THE GUY AND BRING HIM BEFORE THEIR 'GRAND INQUISITOR'!

"AND GUESS WHAT?

"RIGHT. NO KEY.

"WHEN THE GUY ESCAPES AGAIN, THE HIGH PRIEST GOES **BANANAS**! SENDS OUT HIS KILLER ROBOTS TO RETRACE THE THIEF'S STEPS AND FIND EITHER HIM OR THE KEY--**OR BOTH**!

"THIS TIME THEY DON'T STOP FOR ANYTHING, OR ANY**BODY**!

"WITH ALL THE **DESTRUCTION** GOING ON, WE DECIDE TO STEP IN AND HELP **STOP** IT! A FRIEND OF MINE HELPS SET UP OUR LITTLE '**WINDOW**' SO THAT I CAN APPEAR WHERE THE 'BOTS DO: **JUST MOMENTS AHEAD OF THEM**!"

9

"THE REST--

YOUR TURN! WHAT'S *YOUR* NAME?

IT'S JENNY-- *JENNY WEAVER*.

THIS IS ALL SO *CONFUSING!* I MEAN--YOU'VE ANSWERED ALL MY QUESTIONS--

--BUT...

"--YOU ALREADY KNOW,"

...IT'S ALL SO *BIG*--SO *NEW!* I NEVER DREAMED ANYTHING LIKE THIS *EXISTED!* BUT IT'S ALL THERE--AS REAL AS *I* AM!

YUP.

Y'KNOW--I ALWAYS THOUGHT THE WORLD WAS SO SMALL. *DULL, DRAB* AND *BORING.* I THOUGHT I KNEW EVERYTHING I NEEDED TO KNOW.

GUESS I WAS *WRONG.*

KIND OF *SHAKES* YOU UP, HUNH?

OH, *NO!*

NO, I *LIKE* IT! I MEAN, I WANT TO LEARN *MORE!* TAKE ME BACK WITH YOU, *PLEASE?!*

WELL, I--

PLEASE?!

O.K.! O.K.! NO PROBLEM! IF THAT'S WHAT YOU *WANT!*

I'M A PRETTY GOOD *TOUR-GUIDE* ACTUALLY. I'VE BEEN AROUND A LOT MORE THAN *MOST KIDS* MY AGE, I COULD SHOW YOU...

UH... YOU LOOK KIND OF PALE... WHAT--

B-B-BE- BEHIND Y-Y-YOU--

10

RAWHR!

LOOK OUT!

SMAK!

NGGKK!

CHOK!

HE'LL KILL HIM! UNLESS--

KLING

...THE GUN!

"ONE CHARGE LEFT" HE SAID!

ONE CHANCE--

11

FOOM

≈Whew!

HNH?
...OH SORRY.

I'LL GET--
...

≈Giggle≈

Uh...um,
WELL UH...
I, ah...um...

KLINK!

GOTTA GO!

NO,
WAIT!

WHEEEEEE-OOOO-EE

HE'S GONE!
BUT WHAT--?

POLICE SIRENS??

EEE-OOOOO-EEEE-OO

HEAR THAT?! NOW YOU'RE GONNA CATCH IT, YOU ROWDY KIDS! THIS TIME I MEAN BUSINESS! I'VE HAD ENOUGH FROM YOU!

AAAH, SHUT UP!

HEY, SIS, WHERE'VE YOU BEEN?? YOU HEAR THOSE EXPLOSIONS? MAN!

HE'S GONE...

EEE

AND LOOK WHAT I FOUND LYING AROUND!

I THINK IT'S GOLD!

OH MY GOD! THE KEY!

GIMME THAT!

SNATCH

HEY!

GET BACK HERE, YOU! THAT'S MY K--!?

HEY, WHAT THE %@#! IS THAT??

ZOT, WAIT! I'M COMING THROUGH!

HOLD IT, YOU RUFFIANS! YOU WON'T GET AWAY FROM...HEY, WHAT THE %@#!--??

HALT! POLICE!

SIS, DON'T GO IN THERE!!

ZOT!!

OOOOPH!

HOLD IT!

MP!

HEY, YOU!! FREEZE!!

I SAID FR--??

VRRRP!

WHAT THE %@#!--??

??

PING!

ON EARTH, THE SCENE IS PEACEFUL AGAIN,... IF A LITTLE CONFUSED.

⑬

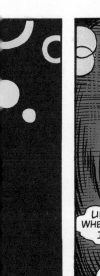

SIS? YOU ALL RIGHT?

UNH... WHERE AM I?

YOU'RE HOME, JENNY.

MY HOME, THAT IS.

ZOT! AND BUTCH! THEN IT WASN'T ALL A DREAM, WAS IT?

NOPE! ALL TRUE!

AND ALL THOSE TALL BUILDINGS AND EVERYTHING?

THAT WAS THE CITY.

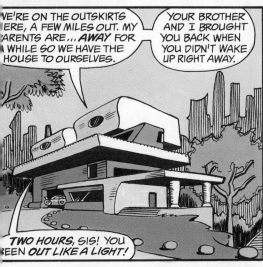

WE'RE ON THE OUTSKIRTS HERE, A FEW MILES OUT. MY PARENTS ARE... AWAY FOR A WHILE SO WE HAVE THE HOUSE TO OURSELVES.

YOUR BROTHER AND I BROUGHT YOU BACK WHEN YOU DIDN'T WAKE UP RIGHT AWAY.

TWO HOURS, SIS! YOU BEEN OUT LIKE A LIGHT!

WOULD YOU CARE FOR SOME REFRESHMENTS, MISS?

AAG! WHAT'S THAT?

JENNY, MEET THE BUTLER-- PEABODY.

BLONDIE'S ROBOT HERE SAVED YOUR HIDE, SIS!

WHEN BLONDIE REALIZED HE COULDN'T GET TO YOU IN TIME, HE HAD ROBBIE HERE SWOOP DOWN AND SCOOP YOU RIGHT UP!

YOU OUGHTTA THANK HIM, SHRIMP!

PEABODY WAS JUST DOING HIS JOB. I HAD HIM WAITING JUST IN CASE SOMETHING LIKE THIS HAPPENED.

WE DIDN'T THINK IT'D BE SAFE IF THE WINDOW LED RIGHT BACK TO THE LAB--

--AND SINCE I CAN FLY, WHAT BETTER PLACE ON EARTH THAN--

HEY, WAIT A MINUTE!

YOU CALLED THIS WORLD "EARTH" JUST NOW, AND ALL ALONG YOU'VE BEEN TALKING IN ENGLISH! AND YOU SURE DON'T LOOK VERY ALIEN.

THIS ISN'T ANOTHER WORLD AT ALL, IS IT?

THIS HAS GOT TO BE--!

YUP! YOU GUESSED IT JENNY...

15

WELCOME, ONE AND ALL, TO THE *FAR-FLUNG FUTURE* OF--

--*1965!*

TA-DA!

ON SECOND THOUGHT, MAYBE THIS ISN'T *EXACTLY* THE SAME "EARTH"...

ZACHARY, PERHAPS IF WE ARE THROUGH ENTERTAINING OUR GUESTS, IT MIGHT BE WISE TO RETURN TO THE BUSINESS AT HAND?

YEAH, THIS *KEY* THING.

NOW THAT SIRIUS' CHURCH IS GETTING SOME HEAT FROM INTER-PLANETARY GROUPS, MAYBE--

I'VE *GOT* IT!

WHAT WAS THAT, JEN?

*THE KEY.* I HELD ON...

*THAT'S IT!*

OH BABY! *THAT'S IT!* YOU JUST SAVED EVERYONE A *LOT* OF TROUBLE, KID! I COULD JUST *KISS YOU!*

WATCH IT, BUDDY! THAT'S MY *SISTER* YOU'RE TALKIN' TO!

OH, EASE UP, BUTCH...

BORN TO RULE

MAY I SUGGEST, ZACHARY, THAT WE RETURN THIS ITEM TO ITS PROPER PLACE, IMMEDIATELY.

WELL, MAYBE IN A LITTLE WHILE, PEABODY, OLD PAL. SURELY IT COULDN'T HURT TO DO A LITTLE *SIGHTSEEING* FIRST, HMM?

I SUSPECT IT WOULD BE EQUALLY SIMPLE TO SIGHTSEE *AFTER* RETURNING THE KEY, ZACHARY.

OH, O.K. WE'LL SIGHTSEE ON THE WAY. HOW'S *THAT* SOUND?

IT SOUNDS AS IF YOU'RE QUITE DECIDED ON THE MATTER...

AWW, C'MON! WHERE'S YOUR SENSE OF *FUN?*

I'M THE STANDARD MODEL, ZACHARY. "FUN" WAS OPTIONAL.

OH... YEAH.

WELL, ALL RIGHT THEN. LET'S TAKE OFF.

I WISH I COULD DRIVE THIS THING *MYSELF*, BUT PEABODY WON'T LET ME WITHOUT A LICENSE.

I DON'T GET IT, ZOT. I THOUGHT PEABODY WOULD DO ANYTHING YOU TOLD HIM TO.

≡Ahem≡

UH, PEABZ IS A LITTLE *TOUCHY* ABOUT THAT, JEN. YOU SEE, ORIGINALLY, HE WAS MEANT AS A KIND OF *STAND-IN PARENT*. BUT WE--THAT IS, ME AND A FRIEND OF MINE--SORT OF *REPROGRAMMED* HIM A BIT.

NOW HE LETS ME GET OUT AND HAVE ADVENTURES, BUT--

--WELL, I HAVE TO BE, UH... *ESCORTED*, I GUESS.

HOW'S THE VIEW?

GREAT!

SO ZOT, WHEN ARE WE GOING TO *MEET* THIS FRIEND OF YOURS?

OH, YOU'LL MEET *EVERYONE*, SOONER OR LATER. WE HAVE LOTS OF TIME.

I WISH BLONDIE'D PUT THE TOP DOWN. IT'S *FREEZING* OUT HERE.

"TIME"?

I *ALWAYS* HAD TIME. *THE REST OF MY LIFE*, I HAD. *BUT NOW I HAVE SOMETHING TO DO* WITH IT. SOMEONE TO *SPEND* IT WITH, MAYBE.

AND WHAT A PLACE TO SPEND IT IN!

Y'KNOW, BUTCH...I DON'T THINK WE'RE IN KANSAS ANYMORE.

HUH?

FORGET IT...

AS THE SHIP DRAWS NEARER THE POLISHED METAL SPIRES OF "THE CITY," JENNY WONDERS...

17

...WAS THERE JUST THE SLIGHTEST GLIMMER OF SOMETHING...EMERALD?

YES INDEED, MR. COUNCILMAN. I HAVE SOMETHING I BELIEVE YOU'LL ALL WANT TO HAVE A LOOK AT.

BUT FIRST I HAVE A FEW ITEMS I'D LIKE TO DISCUSS.

EARLIER TODAY, I CONFRONTED A SQUADRON OF ROBOTS FROM *SIRIUS IV* AS THEY WERE ABOUT TO TRAMPLE AN INNOCENT GIRL TO *DEATH* IN THEIR RECKLESS SEARCH FOR SIRIUS IV'S *GOLDEN KEY.*

WHO *IS* THIS BOY??

*DESTROYED* THE ROBOTS, OF COURSE, KNOWING THAT THE *DAMAGE* WOULD HAVE CONTINUED UNTIL THEIR *"SEARCH"* WAS COMPLETE.

IN A MOMENT I'LL BE MAKING ALL FURTHER VIOLENCE *UNNECESSARY;* BUT FIRST I WOULD LIKE TO SUGGEST--

-THAT THE SIRIUS LEADERSHIP BE HELD *RESPONSIBLE* FOR THE ACTIONS OF ITS CHURCH OFFICIALS--

--AND ALL REPAIRS AND REPAYMENTS BE REFERRED TO THOSE AGENCIES EXCLUSIVELY.

*WHAT*?! I OBJECT! WHAT RIGHT DOES THIS-- THIS *BOY* HAVE TO MAKE THESE SUGGESTIONS?

WELL, I DON'T KNOW ABOUT "RIGHTS", SIR, BUT I DO HAVE *ONE THING* YOU OUGHT TO RESPECT--

OH, NO! WHERE *IS* IT??

I HAD IT RIGHT HERE.

--I HAVE THE KEY!

≳Gasp!≲

!

IF THIS IS SOME *JOKE* OF YOURS, BOY--!

NO JOKE, COUNCILMAN...

JENNY, IF YOU PLEASE...?

ZOT, I DON'T KNOW HOW TO SAY THIS, BUT-- 21

HA! HA! FLEE, COWARDLY HEATHEN!

NOT FOR LONG, BOZO!

≈OOK!≈ ≈OOK!≈

≈OOOK!≈

≈AK!≈ ≈AK!≈

'LL OP THIS OMAN!

≈AARG-OOK!≈

HA! FAT CHANCE!

HA! HA! HA! HA!

≈AAK!≈

N'T GET IT PEABODY. DIDN'T ZOT ARGE HIS GUN? WHY DOESN'T HE ...STUN THE GUY OR SOMETHING?

ZACHARY'S WEAPON HAS ONLY ONE SETTING: DESTROY. THUS HE WILL NOT USE IT ON HIS FELLOW HUMANS...

...EVEN TERRIBLY RUDE ONES SUCH AS--

OH, PARDON ME, MISS.

ZACHARY, I'VE DETECTED SOMETHING OF INTEREST.

PEABODY SPEAKS, AS ALWAYS, IN A LOW MONOTONE, BUT ACROSS THE ROOM HIS WORDS REACH ZOT'S TINY EARPIECE AT A VOLUME ONLY ZOT CAN HEAR...

I BELIEVE IF YOU APPROACH THIS FELLOW--

"APPROACH" HIM?? THIS BETTER BE GOOD!

mmmmmm

GIMME THAT GUN OF HIS, PEABODY.

THERE!

SO MUCH FOR *THAT* LITTLE TROUBLE-MAKER.

TRASH!

BAH!

A *FEEBLE GESTURE*, YOU *HAIRLESS HEATHEN!!*

KEEP IT UP, *FRUITCAKE*, IF YOU WANT TO END UP LOOKING LIKE *THIS!*

*HA!* YOU AND WHAT ARMY!

Uh... ZOT?

YES, JENNY-- WHAT'S UP?

ZOT, I...I'M SORRY. I'VE LOST IT. I'VE LOST THE KEY.

OH... Uh...

Heh, Heh.

SORRY ABOUT THAT, GUYS. NO KEY, AFTER ALL!

Ahem!

Hmm....

20

WELL, IN VIEW OF *TODAY'S EVENTS*, IT'S CLEAR THAT THIS KEY IS GOING TO *CONTINUE* CAUSING PROBLEMS UNTIL IT'S FOUND.

PERHAPS THE COUNCIL *SHOULD PARTICIPATE* IN THE SEARCH-- AS ZARBIM SUGGESTED-- AFTER ALL.

AND WILL OUR OPERATIONS BE IN THE HANDS OF *MERE WHELPS* LIKE THIS ONE??

*HEY,* HAPPY TO BE OF SERVICE!

WHATEVER.

ALL THOSE IN FAVOR?

AYE! AYE! AYE! AYE! AYE! AYE! AYE! AYE! AYE! AYE! AYE!

≥OOK!≤

Uh-oh...

≥Gasp!≤

*IT'S NOT OVER YET!!*

YOU CAN [ME] IT ALL ON-- SCOTT McCLOUD WRITER/ARTIST • C. McCARTHY LETTERER • D. McFARLING COLORIST • KURT BUSIEK CONSULTANT • CAT⊕ AND DEAN EDITORS

THIS IS JENNY WEAVER. SHE'S FROM *OUR* EARTH (THE *NORMAL* ONE).

JENNY WAS JUST OUT FOR A WALK ONE DAY--

--WHEN SHE BUMPED INTO *THIS* GUY. HIS NAME IS *ZOT* AND HE'S THE HERO, OF COURSE. NAME'S ON THE COVER AND EVERYTHING...

BUTCH, HERE, IS JENNY'S BROTHER. HE JUST CAME ALONG FOR THE RIDE WHEN JENNY ENTERED ZOT'S WORLD.

HE DIDN'T COUNT ON BEING TURNED INTO A CHIMPANZEE--

BY *THIS* GUY, WHO DID SO, *PRIMARILY* BECAUSE HE'S CRAZY, BUT ALSO BECAUSE HE BELONGS TO A CULT--

WHICH SENT HIM IN SEARCH OF A CERTAIN *KEY* WHICH THEY THOUGHT OUR HEROES HAD POSSESSION OF.

(WHICH THEY *DID*, IN FACT, THOUGH ONLY TEMPORARILY) A LOT OF PEOPLE WOULD LIKE TO GET A HOLD OF THIS LITTLE KEY--

--BECAUSE, AS LEGEND HAS IT, IT'S THE ONLY KEY THAT CAN OPEN THE FAMOUS *"DOORWAY AT THE EDGE OF THE UNIVERSE."*

A LOT OF *RELIGIONS* HAVE SPRUNG UP AROUND THIS *TIMELESS WONDER* AND MANY PEOPLE TAKE IT VERY SERIOUSLY.

THAT'S WHY THE *OWNERS* OF THE KEY --OF A PLANET CALLED *SIRIUS IV*--WERE NOT AMUSED--

--WHEN IT WAS *STOLEN* RIGHT FROM UNDER THEIR NOSES BY AN AS YET *UNSEEN* CRIMINAL.

ARBIM BORLOCK IS THE PLANETARY AMBASSADOR FROM SIRIUS IV AND ABOUT AS MUCH FUN AS A *ROOT-CANAL*.

YOU'LL SEE.

JAMES GOODMAN IS ZOT'S EARTH'S REPRESENTATIVE AND DEFINITELY ON THE SIDE OF *ORDER* AND *REASON*, (THOUGH HE REALLY OUGHT TO TAKE A *VACATION*).

FINALLY THERE IS PEABODY, ZOT'S ROBOT BUTLER, WHO IS ABOUT TO SAY SOMETHING *IMPORTANT*.

SO *LISTEN UP...*

--SOMETHING RATHER *IMPORTANT*, ZACHARY.

SPECIFICALLY, I HAD DETECTED A FAINT BUT UNIQUE SORT OF *RADIANT ENERGY* EMITTING FROM SIRIUS IV'S *GOLDEN KEY* WHILE IT WAS IN OUR POSSESSION

*HMM!* THAT *COULD* BE IMPORTANT!

*INDEED!*

BUT HOW TO USE THIS INFORMATION IN *LOCATING* THE SACRED KEY...?

WELL, LET'S SEE NOW...

PERHAPS, SEARCH CREWS COULD BE EQUIPPED TO *DETECT* THAT RADIATION.

ONCE DETECTED...

PRECISELY. WITH PROPER *TRIANGULATION*, TWO SHIPS COULD PIN-POINT THE KEY'S LOCATION WITHIN *MINUTES*.

THERE YA GO!

EVOLVED *SCUM!*

WE'LL GET YOU, *YET!*

*EEK!!AAAK!! AAAK!!EEK!!*

DON'T LET HIM *SCARE* YOU BUTCH.

BORN TO RULE

HE CAN'T TURN YOU INTO A *CHIMP* IF YOU'RE *ALREADY* A CHIMP.

EXCUSE ME, BUT WE'RE HAVING A *SERIOUS DISCUSSION* OVER THERE.

COULD YOU TRY TO KEEP IT *DOWN* A BIT?

*HEATHEN!*

THANKS.

ONE THING'S FOR *SURE.* WHOEVER'S THE *BRAINS* OF HIS OUTFIT, IT ISN'T *HIM!* HE CERTAINLY COULDN'T *REBUILD* THIS GUN AND *REVERSE* ITS EFFECT ON BUTCH.

HA! HA! HA!

≡SIGH!≡ ≡AK! AK!≡

NOW, THAT'S *ANOTHER* THING YOU MIGHT WANT TO DO. IF YOU CAN *SNIFF OUT* THE *REST* OF THIS GUY'S *CULT*, MAYBE YOU CAN FIND OUT HOW *THEY* KNEW THE KEY WAS ON ITS WAY HERE.

THAT *IS* STILL A MYSTERY...

YES...

HMM...

MAYBE *THEY* KNOW *SOMETHING* WE *DON'T* 'BOUT THIS DUMB K--

ENOUGH!

YOU'VE DONE YOUR *GOOD DEED* FOR THE DAY, BOY! WHY ARE YOU STILL HERE?

WHAT??

WHY AREN'T YOU IN *GRADE-SCHOOL* WHERE YOU *BELONG?!*

'CAUSE I'M ON *VACATION,* MORON! WHAT'S *YOUR* EXCUSE?!

I MEAN IT, *BONE-HEAD!* I'M STARTING TO GET--!

--STARTING TO GET--

HOLD IT... KEEP CONTROL... COUNT TEN.

NOT *WORTH* IT...

SORRY. NEVER MIND.

I'LL GO.

AND SO, ONCE PEABODY HAS SUPPLIED HIS INFORMATION TO THE PROPER COMPUTERS--

SO LONG, ZOT! LET US KNOW IF YOUR UNCLE HAS ANY LUCK WITH THAT GUN!

O.K.! GOOD LUCK ON *YOUR* END!

HEATHENS! NON-BELIEVERS! FAITHLESS FOOLS! HAIRLESS--!

SHUT UP!!!

YOU SAID IT.

HEY, LOOK, DALLIT! THAT MUST BE ZOT!

ZOWIE! AH'LL BET YORE RIGHT, BERBAX!

I HEAR THAT KID'S QUITE A HERO AROUND HERE.

YEAH! AND ONLY JUST IN HIS TEENS! GAWRSH!

YES, SIR, I HAVE THEM SPOTTED. NOW VEERING DUE WEST AS PREDICTED.

GOOD! GOOD! HEADED FOR THE BOY'S UNCLE'S HOME, NO DOUBT!

THERE HE GOES, DALLIT!

SHALL I CONTINUE TO FOLLOW HIM, SIR?

FOLLOW?

SURE IS SPEEDY!

YES, YES! I SIMPLY MUST HAVE THAT KEY, AND I'M CERTAIN ZOT IS THE ONE TO FIND IT AGAIN...YES!

TAIL HIM IN YOUR USUAL WAY.

VERY GOOD SIR. OVER AND OUT.

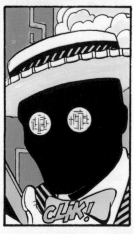

CLIK!

AND AS THE SPRAWLING MIDDAY CROWDS PLACIDLY GLIDE TOWARD THEIR RESPECTIVE DESTINATIONS, ONLY ONE OF THEM NOTICES AN ODDLY DRESSED GENTLEMAN WHO CALMLY STEPS TO ONE SIDE...

AND VANISHES INTO A WINDOWLESS METAL WALL.

?

7

HERE WE ARE!

HOLY--! THAT'S A *HOUSE??* THIS UNCLE OF YOURS MUST BE *RICH!*

A *LITTLE...* MOSTLY JUST *AMBITIOUS.* HE BUILT IT *HIMSELF!*

C'MON UP THE STAIRS. MAYBE WE CAN *SURPRISE* HIM!

HEY *MAX!!*

MREEOW!

HMM...

ARE YOU SURE HE'S *HOME?*

USUALLY *IS...*

I DON'T *KNOW* ABOUT THIS PLACE, ZOT.

SQUAK!! AK!!

*ZACHARY,* MY BOY!!

MAX!

SO! DECIDED TO PAY THE OLD NUTCASE A VISIT, EH, ZACH?

WELL IT'S GOOD TO SEE YOU, KID. IT'S BEEN GETTING SO DULL AROUND HERE I'VE HAD TO RESORT TO *ADULTS* FOR COMPANY!

PAT! PAT!

MAKES ME SICK.

WELL, AT LEAST THEY'LL NEVER MAKE YOU GROW UP.

GOD, I *HOPE* NOT! BUT, NOW, JUST LOOK AT *YOU!*

MY, HOW YOU'VE GROWN!

C'MON, IT'S ONLY BEEN A WEEK AND A HALF!

NOW, LISTEN, I BROUGHT SOME GUESTS--

YES, I SEE! HEH, HEH...

ALWAYS TRYIN' TO FIX ME UP WITH THE LADIES, EH? YOU *LITTLE RASCAL*, YOU!

MAX, MEET JENNY! JENNY, THIS IS MY CRAZY UNCLE MAX.

HI!

HI, YOURSELF!

JENNY'S FROM THAT PLACE WE THOUGHT WAS A PAST EARTH BUT IT TURNED OUT TO BE A SORT OF *ALTERNATE* EARTH.

HMM... I SEE.

SO WHAT BRINGS *YOU* HERE, BONZO?

OH, *PLEASE* DON'T *SCARE* HIM!

AK!

BUTCH IS HIS NAME, AND UP UNTIL A WHILE AGO HE WAS JENNY'S *BROTHER*--A *HUMAN!* THAT'S WHY WE'RE HERE!

AND SHORTLY--

LUCKY FOR *YOU*, MY FURRY FRIEND, I JUST RECENTLY *PERFECTED* THIS PORTABLE *TRANSLATOR-UNIT.*

ASSUMING YOU'RE STILL *THINKING* LIKE A HUMAN, THIS LITTLE *DOO-HICKEY* OUGHT TO HELP YOU *SPEAK* LIKE ONE, TOO!

THAT'S MY UNCLE! ALWAYS *INVENTING* SOMETHING!

NOW, THIS WON'T HURT A BIT...

*CLIK!*

*OWW!*

OH, SORRY.

IT DID *TOO* HURT, YOU OLD *QUACK!*

%#@£! WHAT A BUNCH OF *TURKEYS!* FIRST *BLONDIE,* HERE, OFF AN' *BREAKS* THE ONLY #@£%.!X THING THAT CAN TURN ME BACK TO *NORMAL,* THEN EVERYBODY JUST STANDS AROUND *TALKING* FOR A #@.£%.!8 HOUR--

THEN BLONDIE TAKES ME TO HIS UNCLE, THE *WITCH-DOCTOR!* BIG #@!£%.!8 HELP! %#@£!

MAKES ME WANT TO THR--*MMMF.*

I THINK WHAT BUTCH IS TRYING TO SAY IS: "*THANK YOU VERY MUCH FOR YOUR KIND ASSISTANCE.*"

ANY TIME!

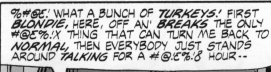

=*MMMFF!*=

HEY, ZACH, WANT TO SEE WHAT THE *BACK-YARD* LOOKS LIKE THIS MONTH?

SOUNDS GOOD.

10

OH, I FIGURE I'LL BE SATISFIED WHEN I'M PUSHING UP THE DAISIES. HAVEN'T HAD A CHANCE TO TRY THAT, THOUGH...TOO BUSY *LIVING*, I GUESS

HOW 'BOUT YOU?

...STILL LIVING...

SO, IT'S *GARDENING* NOW, HUH?

I *SWEAR*, MAX, EVER SINCE I CAN REMEMBER YOU WERE *ALWAYS* FINDING SOMETHING *NEW* TO SPEND TIME ON!

THINK YOU'LL *EVER* BE SATISFIED WITH ANY *ONE* THING?

ANY NEWS FROM YOUR FOLKS, ZACH?

*FORGET* ABOUT THAT, MAX! JUST *FORGET* ABOUT IT!

THERE'S *NOT* GOING TO *BE* ANY NEWS, MAX! IT'S JUST *STUPID* TO KEEP ASKING! O.K.? IT'S JUST BEEN *TOO LONG*...

*GOD*, ZACH, I WISH YOU WOULDN'T *TALK* LIKE THAT! YOU'RE MAKING *ME* FEEL OLD!

HOPE'S AN IMPORTANT *PART* OF YOU. YOU CAN'T JUST *THROW IT AWAY* LIKE AN OLD *Q-TIP*.

HANG ON TO WHAT-EVER YOU CAN, ZACH. I KNOW IT'S NOT MUCH, BUT HANG-ON.

OH BOY...

TO THINK HE HAD ME BELIEVING LIFE WAS ACTUALLY *SIMPLE* HERE.

I GUESS EVEN ZOT HAS HIS PROBLEMS. I JUST WISH I KNEW WHAT THEY WERE ALL ABOUT.

HEY, GLOOMY, *WAKE UP!* MAX JUST HAD A GOOD IDEA.' HE FIGURED HE COULD STAY HERE AND SEE ABOUT FIXING THAT *MONKEY-GUN*--

--AND IN THE MEANTIME, WE COULD ALL DO A LITTLE MORE *SIGHT-SEEING!* HOW ABOUT IT?

AH...O.K. FINE BY ME.

11.

A SWIFT FLIGHT LATER.

WOW! THESE PLATFORMS GO ON FOR MILES! AND INSIDE ALL THESE SHELTERS--?

GAMES.

THIS SECTION IS ALL GAMES.

WHAT KIND, BLONDIE?

WELL, LET'S SEE--

"--WE'VE GOT THE OLD STYLE SCREEN GAMES, OF COURSE..."

"THEN THERE ARE VARIOUS HARDWARE AND HOLOGRAM DISPLAYS..."

"HAND-TO-HAND COMBAT AND STUFF...YOU NAME IT, THEY'VE GOT IT!

"WANT TO TAKE A LOOK?

WHAT'S THAT ONE?

OH, THAT'S A GAME CALLED SURVIVALAX.

WEIRD.

DOESN'T IT LOOK LIKE FUN, ROBBIE?

THRILLING.

IS THAT A REAL GUY IN THERE, BLONDIE?

35:59

YUP! AND ACCORDING TO THE MONITOR HE'S BEEN INSIDE NEARLY 36 HOURS!

36 HOURS? HE MUST BE OUT OF HIS MIND!

8 SECONDS TO GO!

GO! GO!

35:59

J WOW!

I DON'T BELIEVE IT!

7!

6!

5!

4!

HE'S GOING TO DO IT!

35:59

AA!

HE'S GOING TO DO IT--!

3!! 2!! 1!!

ZERO!!!

NEW WORLD'S RECORD!

YAY!

YAHOO!

36:00

WHOA!

THAT KID'S A WIZARD WHOEVER HE IS!

AWESOME!

YOW!!

BOY, THAT GUY'S REALLY GOIN' FOR BROKE! AIN'T IT ENOUGH TO MAKE YOU WET YER PANTS?

I WOULDN'T KNOW.

HEY, WE'LL MEET YOU GUYS BACK HERE IN AN HOUR, O.K.? JENNY AND I ARE GOING TO CHECK OUT SOME RIDES.

YEAH, GO AHEAD, BLONDIE! ME 'AN' CHROME DOME'LL HAVE A GREAT TIME TOGETHER, RIGHT, PAL?

ONE HOUR, ZACHARY.

AND, A SHORT WALK LATER...

THIS USED TO BE MY FAVORITE SPOT WHEN I WAS A LITTLE KID.

DID YOU COME OFTEN?

MY FOLKS BROUGHT ME ALMOST EVERY WEEKEND DURING VACATIONS.

I LIVED FOR THOSE WEEKENDS.

I WAS A PRETTY GOOD KID OVERALL. BUT IF ANYTHING GOT IN THE WAY OF OUR LITTLE WEEKLY TRIPS--

--BOY, WOULD I SCREAM!

THANK YOU, SIR.

CLINK!

AHA! YOU DO HAVE TO PAY AROUND HERE! I WAS STARTING TO WONDER!

13.

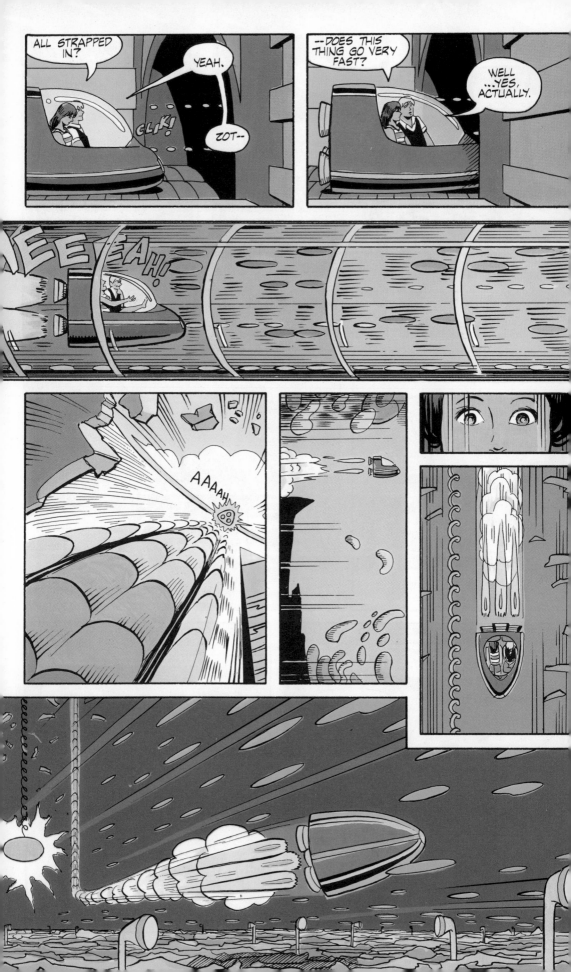

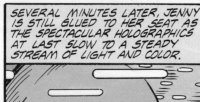

SEVERAL MINUTES LATER, JENNY IS STILL GLUED TO HER SEAT AS THE SPECTACULAR HOLOGRAPHICS AT LAST SLOW TO A STEADY STREAM OF LIGHT AND COLOR.

Y'KNOW, THIS USED TO BE MY *FAVORITE RIDE*...

IT WAS THE ONLY ONE MY *MOTHER* WOULD COME ALONG FOR. WE'D GET A *TWO-SEATER* LIKE THIS ONE AND I'D SIT ON HER LAP FOR FREE.

I'D ASK THEM IF I COULD REACH OUTSIDE...JUST FOR A *SECOND*. THEY NEVER LET ME...

I THOUGHT IF I COULD JUST *GRAB ONTO* THESE SHOOTING LIGHTS, THAT SOMETHING *MAGIC* WOULD HAPPEN... I DON'T KNOW *WHAT*...

I DIDN'T KNOW THEN THAT IT WAS ALL AN *ILLUSION*...

STUPID KID...

WE WERE HAPPY THEN... I THOUGHT WE'D ALWAYS BE HAPPY THAT WAY...

SOMETHING *CHANGED*, THOUGH, DIDN'T IT?

NO ANSWER...

D'YA WANT TO TALK ABOUT IT, ZOT?

I DON'T KNOW IF I *CAN* TALK ABOUT IT...

TRY.

17.

CATCH YOU *LATER*, JEN!

AND DON'T *WORRY*, THEY'LL *SEND* SOMEONE TO *PICK YOU UP*!

≥SIGH!≤

ZZZZZ--ɛ

!?

*CLIK!*

SORRY TO *DISTURB* YOU IN YOUR *QUARTERS*, ZARBIM, BUT ZOT'S ROBOT JUST SENT US SOME *NEWS*.

WHAT IS IT, GOODMAN?

THEY THINK THEY MAY HAVE LOCATED YOUR *KEY*. THE ROBOT IS *RELAYING* THE *COORDINATES* RIGHT NOW.

*EXCELLENT!* I'LL BE WITH YOU *SHORTLY.* FIRST I HAVE SOME *BUSINESS* TO ATTEND TO.

SURE. SEE YOU IN A WHILE.

CLAK! CLAK! CLA

YEAH, COME IN!

*DREEEEP!*

OH, HELLO, UNCLE...

IT IS *TIME*, YOUNG PRINCE.

18

UNCLE, DO YOU THINK....? MAYBE *THIS* TIME I SHOUDN'T--?

YOU WILL BE READY IN *FIVE MINUTES.*

YES, UNCLE.

HEY, *LOOK!* COMING OUT OF THE *TUNNEL.*

MUST BE THAT *"ZOT"* KID!

HI, GUYS!

*YAHOO!* GO *GET* 'IM, BLONDIE!

YES SIR, JUST ENTERING THE *MACHINE.*

"DO YOU THINK HE HAS A LEAD ON THE KEY?"

"YES, SIR. IT LOOKS LIKELY!"

HEY, YOU CAN'T--!

SHALL I FOLLOW HIM IN?

NO, NO, WAIT!

YES, WAIT...

"LET'S JUST...*WATCH* FOR A WHILE..."

36:26

19.

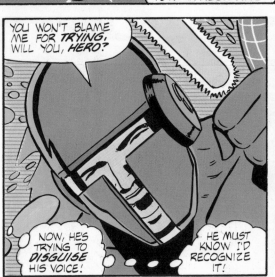

BUT--

--IF I COULD PLAY IT *THEN*--

*SNAP!*

--I CAN PLAY IT *NOW*!!

BETTER *HURRY*, THOUGH, I LOST A LOT OF *POINTS* BACK THERE!

IF I LOSE TOO MANY I'LL JUST *BLINK* OUT OF THE GAME.

*HMM*...JUMPING DOWN TO LEVEL 2! WELL, I KNOW MY *GUN* WON'T WORK IN THIS PLACE...

...LET'S SEE IF MY *BOOT-JETS* WILL.

*GREAT!* NOW, AT LEAST I CAN *FLY!*

*YEAH, LIKE A BIRD--*

*HRUUNK!*

--YOU *TURKEY!*

HA! HA! HA!

AND SO IT GOES FOR *TWENTY MINUTES* OR SO, WHEN *SUDDENLY*--!

HEY, SOMEBODY ELSE IS JUMPING IN, *PEABZ!*

OH, NO...

WHAT IS IT? WHAT IS IT?

"OH SIR, IT'S THAT *POMPOUS WHELP,* PRINCE *DRUFUS* OF SIRIUS IV!"

"WHO?"

"DRUFUS IS HIS PLANET'S RATHER *FEEBLE* ANSWER TO ZOT, SIR. MORE A *MEDIA PLO[Y]* THAN ANYTHING ELSE."

"IT'S NO DOUBT *IMPORTANT* TO THE SIRUSIAN RULES THAT ONE OF THEIR OWN CITIZENS FIND THE "SACRED KEY" BEFORE ZOT DOES!"

"YES, YES... I SEE, I SEE...DO YOU THINK HE MIGHT ACTUALLY SUCCEED?"

"IN A WORD, SIR: *NO!*"

*YAAAAH!*

WHAT THE--? *DRUFUS?!*

FRIEND ZOT! I HAVE C-COME TO HELP YOU IN YOUR BATTLE!

YOU'RE GOING TO HELP *ME?!*

FOR *PETE'S SAKE,* DRUFUS, YOU'RE *DRAWING* ALL THE FIRE OVER *HERE!*

HOW CAN WE *PROTECT* OURSELVES?!

*"WE"* DID A LOT BETTER WHEN IT WAS JUST *ME*--! GRRR...OH, ALL RIGHT, *COME ON!*

COMING.

23.

SOMEBODY, CALL THE *MANAGEMENT!* THOSE GUYS SHOULDN'T BE *IN THERE!*

THEY MAY TURN OFF THE *MACHINE* SOON, SIR, SHALL I TAKE A HAND?

YES DO...*DO!*

ZACHARY!

YES, PEABODY! WHAT'S UP?

I'VE DETECTED A *FOURTH PRESENCE* IN THE GAMING-GRID! ONE OF *IMMENSE* POWER!

OH, *GREAT...*

WELL *WHO*-OR *WHAT*EVER IT IS WILL HAVE TO *WAIT!*

I'VE GOT A *THIEF* TO CATCH.

OH, *NO!*

THAT'S IT, ZOT! *TACKLE* HIM!

OOOF!!

OKAY, *YOU!* WHERE'S THAT *KEY* YMMPH!

SUCKER!

BOY, YOU'RE REALLY *ASKING* FOR IT!

YEAH? WHO GONNA *GIVE* IT TO ME, *BANANA BRAIN?!*

2↓

HOLD ON, FRIEND ZOT!

*OOOF!*

I'LL STOP THIS THIEVING *BLASPHEMER!*

POW!

CHAK!

RRF!

NGF!

FOK!

BMF!

CRAK!

NNNH...*THANKS,* "*FRIEND!*"

I'M SORRY... I...

HA! HA!

DON'T *APOLOGIZE!* GO *GET* HIM!

GO AHEAD -- I'LL BE FINE! I'LL CATCH YOU LATER!

ALL RIGHT, UH...

...*FAREWELL* THEN! I WON'T *DISHONOR* US, BRAVE FRIEND!

=SIGH= HE'S SUCH A *TOOL!* I ALMOST HATED TO DO THIS TO HIM! *ALMOST...*

BUT SOMEHOW I'VE GOT A *HUNCH* THAT MAYBE SIRIUS SHOULDN'T GET THEIR KEY BACK *RIGHT AWAY* --

--AND AS LONG AS OUR *MYSTERIOUS THIEF* LET IT DROP OFF HIM, WHO AM I TO *PASS* IT *UP?*

THERE'S *MORE* TO THIS KEY THAN JUST A *LEGEND.* WHAT IS IT?

WHY DOES EVERYONE *WANT* IT?

ULP!

CLIK!

25.

TURN THAT PAGE..!

S-SOMEONE WAS *HERE*, JUST BEFORE THE *LIGHTS* CAME ON!

WHAT?! WHO--?!

JUST MY *IMAGINATION*... I *GUESS*...I STILL HAVE THE *KEY*, BUT WHERE DID *DRUFUS* AND THE *THIEF* GO?

JENNY, YOU *GOT* HERE! WHAT *HAPPENED*?

THOSE TWO GUYS JUST *BOLTED* OUT THE DOOR AND INTO THE *CROWD*.

GONE?

GOOD... *GOOD*...

WHAT *AM* I UP TO?

OH, WELL! GUESS WE BETTER GET BACK TO *MAX'S* PLACE.

HEY! IT'S THAT *ZOT* KID!

YEAH!

BORN T

HEY, CAN YOU SIGN THIS--?

--MY *SISTER* JUST LOVES--!

WOW!

SAY, AREN'T YOU--?

--STOP FOR A

SAY A FEW--?

SORRY GUYS, NOT TODAY!

GEE, I FORGOT YOU WERE SUCH A *CELEBRITY*!

SHORTLY...

HOME, JAMES! I'VE HAD ENOUGH *CRAZINESS* FOR ONE DAY!

SAME *HERE*!

MY NAME ISN'T "*JAMES*," ZACHARY...

26

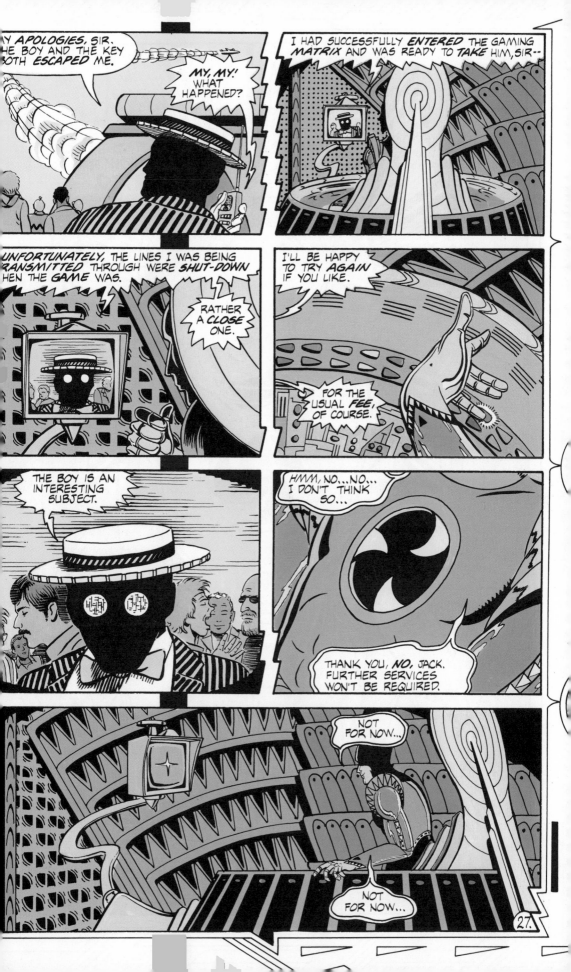

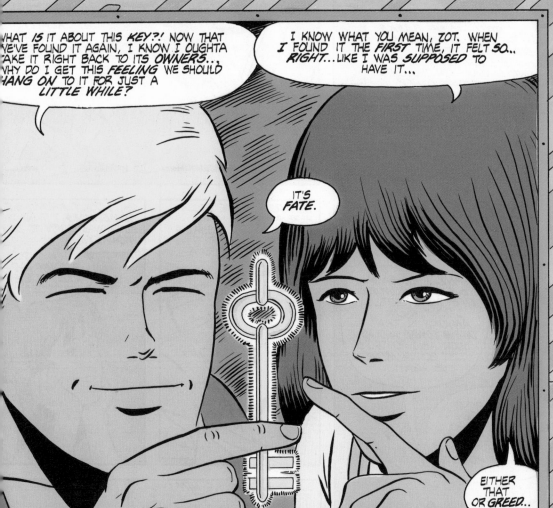

# ART AND SOUL
## •PART ONE•

| CARRIE McCARTHY | DENIS McFARLING | KURT BUSIEK & ADAM PHILIPS | DEAN MULLANEY & CAT YRONWODE |
|---|---|---|---|
| LETTERER | COLORIST | CONSULTANTS | EDITORS |

...OT'S ALWAYS SO *CHEERFUL* AND *REASSURING.* DOESN'T WANT TO SHARE HIS PROBLEMS WITH *ANYONE.* I WISH HE *WOULD,* THOUGH... I WISH HE'D LET ME *HELP...*

SOME *VIEW* HUH, JENNY?

THERE, HE *GOES* AGAIN!

OL' MAX GETS THE *BEST* OF *BOTH* WORLDS HERE!

*BACK-YARD* SIZE OF A *FOOTBALL FIELD* AND RIGHT BY THE *OCEAN* TO *BOOT!*

THIS IS THE *ATLANTIC, ISN'T* IT? IT *FEELS* THE SAME...

S PUSH!

SPLASH!

...EANS DON'T ...RE WHAT *TIME* ...IS... WHO'S ...TTA BE *WHERE* ...D *WHEN...*

...Y IS IT SUCH A ...DEAL TO *US?*

IT DOESN'T *HAVE* TO BE, JEN. THERE'S A WAY OF *LIVING* THAT'S, WELL...

MAX COULD EXPLAIN IT BETTER THAN ME. SOMETHING *ORIENTAL...*

SEEMS THERE'S SO *MUCH* I COULD LEARN HERE...

...ND I'LL HAVE *PLENTY* OF *OPPORTUNITIES,* RIGHT? ...ECAUSE I'LL SEE *YOU* A LOT, *RIGHT?* HMM?

*RIGHT.*

3.

A FEW HOURS AGO, IN THE *CONTINENT* OF *ANTARCTICA*--

--THE GROUND *SHOOK SLIGHTLY*--

--SIX HOLES SLID OPEN--

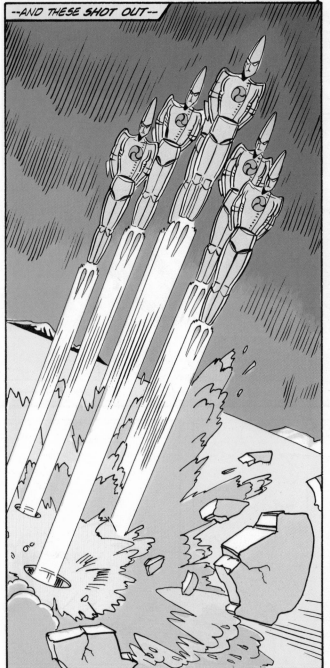

--AND THESE *SHOT OUT*--

--AND BEGAN FLYING *NORTH*.

THEN--

YOU'VE GOT *COMPANY*, ZACH!

BE RIGHT *THERE*, MAX!

*CHRIS!* HEY, HOW ARE YOU? WHERE'S YOUR *BIG BROTHER* VIC? I HAVEN'T SEEN HIM IN WEEKS!

NEITHER HAVE *WE*, ZOT. THAT'S WHY I CAME BY...

HI, MAX! WHAT'S THAT? *LOOKS* LIKE SOME KIND OF *FLUTE*-THING.

INDEED IT *IS*, MY DEAR! BUT, NOT JUST *ANY* KIND OF *FLUTE*-THING!

IT'S CALLED A *SIRUSIAN RECORDER!* WANT A *FREE RECITAL?*

Y'KNOW, VIC TOOK THAT *FIELD-TRIP* TO *SIRIUS IV* OVER *SPRING VACATION*...

YEAH, BUT WEREN'T THEY COMING BACK *TUESDAY?*

THEY *CAME BACK*, BUT VIC WASN'T *WITH* THEM.

WE KNOW IT'S NOT REALLY YOUR *LINE* OF *WORK*, BUT... Y'KNOW...ANYTHING YOU CAN DO TO *HELP*...

YEAH, OF *COURSE*... WOW...

ANYWAY, *MA* THOUGHT YOU SHOULD *KNOW*, BEING HIS *FRIEND* AND ALL...

SURE...

I'LL TELL HER I *FILLED* YOU IN...

OKAY, CHRIS. I'LL SEE WHAT I CAN DO.

COME *BACK*, F THERE'S ANY MORE *NEWS.*

DING-PONG!

DING-PONG!

*THAT* DIDN'T *TAKE* LONG!

QUICK! *CLOSE THE DOOR!*

*VIC!*

*SHH!*

5.

UTCH, ARE YOU *SURE* YOU DON'T WANT TO WEAR THIS SPECIAL *BELT* MAX MADE FOR YOU ESTERDAY? IT'S FOR YOUR OWN PROTECTION!

NO WAY! I CAN TAKE CARE OF MYSELF!

*NEXT* THING I KNOW, YOU'LL WANT ME ON A *LEASH!*

LET *ME* TRY, JENNY...

WELL, ALL RIGHT, BUTCH! BUT I WAS REALLY HOPING THAT YOU'D ACCEPT THIS BELT SO MY NEPHEW WOULD HAVE SOMEONE TO *HELP* HIM IF HE GOT INTO *TROUBLE!*

"HELP"? WELL, I...

O.K. DOC, I'LL USE IT! HOW'S IT WORK?

E SO: THE *RED* BUTTON TRIGGERS A L'IL OLD EAT-BEAM! JUST ENOUGH TO *STUN* SOMEONE...

THE *BLUE* BUTTON ACTIVATES A *FORCE-FIELD.*

AND THE *YELLOW* BUTTON SIGNALS MY *NEPHEW* THAT YOU NEED HELP!

WELL, THANK *YOU,* DR. DOOLITTLE.

NO SWEAT.

OW REMEMBER, ONZO: THAT'S FOR EFENSE ONLY!

OTCHA!

YOU *MAY* NOT NEED IT FOR LONG, THOUGH! I THINK I'VE CONCOCTED A WAY TO RE-HUMANIZE YOU!

REALLY, MAX? THAT'S *GREAT!*

JUST *THINK,* BUTCH! SOON YOU'LL BE ABLE TO GO *HOME* AGAIN!

YEAH, WELL, UH... DON'T RUSH ON *MY* ACCOUNT, DOC.

I WON'T!

SO I HAD TO LOW 3 WEEKS ALLOWANCE ON E DISGUISE UT HE DID A EAL GOOD JOB!

THEN *THAT'S* WHY NONE OF THE "WANTED" PHOTOS MATCH YOU...

WOW... I STILL CAN'T *BELIEVE* IT!

HOMP! HOMP!

Y THIRD-BEST FRIEND IS AN *INTERSTELLAR THIEF!*

WHOAH! HOLD IT, ZACH! I MAY HAVE TAKEN THAT KEY BUT I'M *NO THIEF!* I MEAN...

I KNOW WHAT I DID WAS WRONG AND I'M *SORRY* ABOUT IT! BUT, EVERYTHING *SINCE* THEN I'VE DONE 'CAUSE I *HAD* TO! AND NOW I NEED *HELP... BAD!*

LET ME EXPLAIN...

7.

"I WAS OVER AT **JOSH HACKER'S.** HE'D JUST FINISHED ONE OF THOSE WEIRD GADGETS HE'S ALWAYS **WHIPPING UP.** HE TOLD ME--"

IT EMITS AN **ENERGY FIELD--** ANYONE WEARING THIS IS **INVISIBLE** TO ANY **ELECTRONIC SENSING DEVICES...**

SO I SAID--

HEY! YOU COULD SNEAK IN **ANYWHERE** W THAT! I... I BE YOU COULD EVEN SNATCH THE KE TO "THE DOORW AT THE EDG OF THE UNIVERSE

"AND HE SAID--" NAH, YOU **COULDN'T!** "AND I SAID--" BET YOU **COULD!**

WELL, **YOU** KNOW HOW I AM WHEN I'M ON A **DARE!**

ME AN' "FLOYD" HERE HAD NO TROUBLE GETTING INTO THEIR **MAIN FORTRESS** ON **SIRIUS IV.**

**HUMAN** GUARDS ARE ALL BUT **OBSOLETE** THERE.

WE SLIPPED PAST ABOUT **200 DEDICATED** BUT **USELESS** MACHINES.

AND THE KEY WAS **MINE!**

"THE DEAL WITH JOSH WAS THAT I HIDE OUT UNTIL THE MISSING KEY MADE THE NEWS. SO I HUNG AROUND THE VENTILATION TUNNELS.

"I SWEAR, ZACH, I **NEVER** INTENDED TO KEEP IT MORE THAN A FEW HOURS!"

"BUT, WHILE I WAS **CRAWLING AROUND,** I CAME ACROSS A **SECRET MEETING** OF FOUR OF SIRIUS' HIGHEST RANKING OFFICIALS. THEY HADN'T HEARD THE **NEWS** YET...

"AND, ZACH, WHAT THEY **WERE** SAYING ABOUT THAT KEY AND THEIR PLANS FOR IT WOULD SCARE THE **PANTS** OFF YOU!"

"I LISTENED TO **EVERY WORD--**

"--AND REALIZED WHAT I HAD TO DO!"

"IF I LET THOSE GOONS GET THE KEY BACK, **EARTH** WOULD BE UP THE CREEK IN NO TIME! GET THIS: THEY SAID THAT WHEN THE DOOR IS--"

DING! DO

DING-DONG

JUST A SEC, VIC.

YOU IN SHAPE FOR *COMPANY?*

OH, SURE... ANYONE, SO LONG AS IT'S NOT THAT *IDIOT,* PRINCE DR--

DRUFUS!! WHAT A PLEASANT SURPRISE.

GREETINGS, ZOT! I BRING *GOOD NEWS!*

MY *ROBOTS* AND I TRACED THE *SKULKING THIEF* TO THIS VERY *COUNTY!* SOON WE'LL *HAVE* HIM!

OH, LORD, I'M GONNA DIE!

UH...

FINE CHOICE OF *MUSICAL INSTRUMENTS,* SIR!

THANK YOU.

WE WERE *LED,* OF COURSE, BY THE *SACRED KEY'S* FAINT, BUT *TRACEABLE,* RADIATION!

*UNFORTUNATELY,* THE ONE OF MY ROBOTS *EQUIPPED* TO *DETECT* THE KEY HAS BEGUN TO *MALFUNCTION!*

SAYYY! I'LL BET *I* CAN FIX THAT!

ARE YOU *CRAZY??* DO YOU WANT HIM TO KNOW *I'VE* GOT THE *KEY?*

EH, HEH... PRINCE DRUFUS, THIS IS MY *OLD BUDDY,* VIC TAYLOR!

TRUST ME, ZACH!

GREETINGS!

*BEING* A GOOD FRIEND OF *ZOT* MUST BE A *GREAT* PRIVILEGE, VICTOR!

*SURE* OPENS *SOME DOORS!*

WHY, *GOOD SIR!* DO NOT LET US *INTERRUPT!*

OH, WE'RE NOT *LEAVING,* PRINCE. JUST FINDING A *QUIET CORNER!*

?

IT'S HIS *NATIONAL INSTRUMENT.*

9.

I'D ALMOST *FORGOTTEN* HOW *PRETTY* A SIMPLE *MELODY* CAN BE...

HEY, POPS! HOW ABOUT SOME *REAL* MUSIC?

MAY HAVE A TWINKIE!

THIS *FLUTE-STUFF* IS *WIMPY!*

TAP! TAP!

WIMPY? ARE YOU CALLING MY MUSIC WIMPY!?

UH...YEAH!

OH, YEAH?! YEAH!!

*WIMPY IS IT?!!*
I'LL SHOW YOU!

UH, BUTCH... I DON'T THINK YOU SHOULD'VE SAID THAT...

H-HEY, I DIDN'T *MEAN* NOTHING BY IT...

A FLURRY OF BUTTON-PRESSING AND LEVER-PULLING ENSUES, AND THE WALLS SLIDE BACK, PANELS SLIDE OPEN AND A LOW RUMBLING BEGINS...

CALL MY MUSIC "WIMPY," WILL HE?

"WIMPY"!

HA!

R-REALLY, I WAS J-JUST *KIDDING*...

SO, *VICTOR!* I TAKE IT YOU ARE A STUDENT OF THE *ELECTRONIC ARTS!*

HAVE YOU TAKEN ANY *SPECIAL COURSES?*

OH, I TOOK SOMETHING, YEAH...

OUR FRIEND *ZOT* HAS QUITE A WAY WITH MACHINES, AS WELL.

"HAS THE KEY," YOU MIGHT SAY!

YES! QUITE A VARIED EDUCATION!

NOT "LOCKED IN"?

YES!

CALL *THIS* "WIMPY", BONZO!

"HIS NAME WAS ARTHUR...

"...ARTHUR DEKKER.

"HE AND SARAH WERE *STUDENTS* AT THE *ART-SCHOOL* WHER I TAUGHT. *OUTSIDE* OF CLASS WE BECAME *GOOD FRIENDS.*

"ONE DAY, DURING A *ROUTINE* EXAMINATION, A *RARE CANCER* WAS DETECTED IN ARTHUR. IT HAD BEGUN IN *BOTH HANDS* AND THREATENED TO SPREAD TO THE *REST* OF HIS BODY. IN ORDER TO *PREVENT* THAT, SEVERAL DOCTORS CONCURRED THAT HIS HANDS WOULD NEED TO BE...

...REMOVED.

"*BIONICS* WERE JUST BECOMING PRACTICAL IN *THOSE DAYS,* SO ARTHUR WAS GIVEN *NEW HANDS.*

"HE ADJUSTED *WELL ENOUGH.*

"BUT THE DISEASE *HADN'T* BEEN *STOPPED* AS THE DOCTORS HAD HOPED. ARTHUR WAS BACK IN *SURGERY* WITHIN A MONTH.

THROUGH IT ALL, HE CONTINUED PAINTING—MORE *FURIOUSLY* THAN EVER—IF ONLY TO PAY THE *MEDICAL BILLS.* BUT AS HE DROVE ON, SARAH AND I BEGAN TO NOTICE *SOME CHANGES* TAKING PLACE...

"ARTHUR'S ART WAS BECOMING *LESS SENTIMENTAL*... *MORE DESIGN-ORIENTED* AND *MECHANICAL*. LESS TIED UP WITH *EMOTIONAL CONCERNS*."

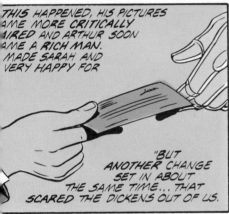

...THIS HAPPENED, HIS PICTURES ...AME MORE *CRITICALLY* ...AIRED AND ARTHUR SOON ...AME A *RICH MAN*. ...MADE SARAH AND ...VERY HAPPY FOR

"BUT *ANOTHER CHANGE* SET IN ABOUT THE SAME TIME... THAT *SCARED THE DICKENS OUT OF US*."

"HE BEGAN TO *LIKE* IT."

...HUR STARTED TO *DESIGN* HIS ...PARTS; ADDING LITTLE *DECORA-* ...TOUCHES HERE AND THERE.

...AS MORE THAN SARAH COULD TAKE.

"I'M NOT SURE IF HE *NOTICED* WHEN *SHE* FINALLY PACKED UP AND *LEFT* HIM.

"AFTER ALL...

"...HE NO LONGER *REQUIRED HUMAN SUBJECTS*."

...NEXT DAY I FOUND ALL OF HIS ...URES OF HER IN THE TRASH ...EATH HIS TOWNHOUSE.

"ARTHUR'S *RICHES* CROSSED THE *BILLION DOLLAR MARK* AT ABOUT THE SAME TIME THE DISEASE REACHED HIS *FACE*.

"WE NO LONGER *SPOKE*...

"I TRIED TO *FORGET* WHAT HAD HAPPENED...

13.

"...AND REMEMBER THOSE HAPPIER DAYS..."

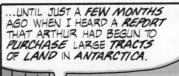

...UNTIL JUST A *FEW MONTHS* AGO WHEN I HEARD A *REPORT* THAT ARTHUR HAD BEGUN TO *PURCHASE* LARGE *TRACTS* OF *LAND* IN ANTARCTICA.

I CAN'T HELP *WONDERING* WHAT HE'S *UP TO,* AND WHETHER WE'LL EVER *CROSS PATHS* AGAIN...

"*IT WORKED FOR A WHILE...*"

*SORRY,* MAX! GUESS I CLOSED THE WRONG *CIRCUIT!*

I *PROMISE* IT WON'T HAPPEN *AGAIN!*

WELL, I'M NOT TAKING ANY *CHANCES,* VIC!

YOU KIDS, TAKE THESE *BOTS* OUTSIDE *NOW!*

YOU *HEARD* HIM, GUYS!

SOON...

MAX...I DON'T MEAN TO *PRY*...BUT THERE'S SOMETHING ABOUT ZOT'S *PARENT'S* I DON'T *UNDERSTAND.*

LIKE WHERE THEY *ARE?*

FOR *STARTERS,* YEAH.

*NEITHER ONE* OF US CAN TELL YOU THAT FOR *CERTAIN,* JENNY. AND AS FOR WHAT WE *DO* KNOW, YOU'D DO BEST TO GET IT FROM ZACH HIMSELF.

THE FACT IS--

--THAT SOMETHING IS *BUGGING* THAT KID THAT EVEN *I* CAN'T EXPLAIN. *ANYTHING* YOU CAN DO TO *UNRAVEL* THAT MYSTERY, I'D GREATLY *APPRECIATE.*

OH, *ONE THING* YOU OUGHT TO *KNOW* ABOUT ZACH, THOUGH. HE'S USED TO BEING *LIKED*--GETS IT *EVERYWHERE* HE GOES --SO WHEN *SOMEONE* COMES ALONG WHO COULD MEAN A LOT *MORE* TO HIM...

...HE'S GOING TO BE A LITTLE *SLOW* TO *NOTICE.*

*"BE PATIENT, JENNY."*

SO, ZACH! YOU GONNA TAKE OFF AND *FIND* THIS *"TREACHEROUS THIEF"?!*

SURE, VIC.

DON'T PUSH YOUR *LUCK.*

YOUR *ASSISTANCE* WILL BE *GREATLY APPRECIATED,* ZOT! WE MAKE A *FINE TEAM!*

AND AS SOON AS VICTOR *REPAIRS* MY *ROBOT* WE CAN BE OFF ON *THE HUNT* AGAIN!

I'M SURE THAT WE CAN RECOVER THE *SACRED KEY* IN *NO TIME* AT ALL.

YEAH, I COULD PROBABLY FIND IT *PRETTY QUICK...*

QUICK AS YOU CAN FIND YOUR OWN *BACK-POCKET--*

--YOU MIGHT SAY.

AH...YES...

ZACHARY, WERE YOU EXPECTING *OTHER* VISITORS?

VIC, CUT IT OUT!

VISITORS? NO, NOT REALLY.

THEN WHO ARE--?

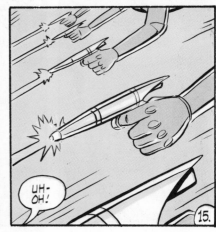

UH-OH!

15.

16.

TRY AND HIT 'EM *DEAD CENTER!* NOT AT AN *ANGLE!*

LIKE *SO!*

*THAT'S SLOWING 'EM.!!*

...ACH! ...N'T LET ...EM *TRAMPLE* ...E AZALEAS!

BUT HOW DO WE *STOP* THEM?! AAAAAHH!!!

...EED ...ELP?

ALL RIGHT..!

...WHERE'D I PUT THAT *MAGNETIC GRENADE?!*

...! YES!! PLEASE!!!

AH, *HERE* IT IS!

...TAND BACK, KIDS!

YOU *TOO,* PEABODY! CLEAR THAT AREA!

K-CLINK!

THIS'LL TAKE CARE OF THOSE *BOTS!*

CLK!

SPROING!

17.

YUP, THAT TOOK CARE OF THEM.

AWW, JUST *LOOK* AT MY *AZALEAS!*

JUST LOOK AT MY *ROBOTS...*

OH, WHAT ARE *MOM* AND *DAD* GOING TO SAY? I'M SOME *GREAT PRINCE*...THIS WAS SUPPOSED TO BE *EASY...*

THEY SAID IT'D BE *EASY* WITH THE ROBOTS...

YOU *STILL* THINK IT'S *RIGHT* FOR US TO KEEP THE KEY, VIC?

*YES!* I'M *SURE*, ZACH! AFTER WHAT I HEARD ON *SIRIUS IV*--!

*SORRY*, VIC-- BUT IT DOESN'T MATTER *WHAT* THEIR PLANS ARE. IT'S *THEIR* KEY AND WE'VE GOT TO *RESPECT* THEIR *RIGHTS!*

WE CAN TELL YOUR STORY TO SOME PEOPLE WHO OUGHT TO *KNOW*, BUT FIRST THE KEY GOES BACK TO *SIRIUS!* I'M SORRY.

SO AM *I*, ZACH, 'CAUSE I CAN'T LET YOU *DO* THIS.

MMM...WITH A LITTLE *RIGGING* THIS MIGHT MAKE A GOOD *FOUNTAIN...*

NOW *THAT'S* THINKING *CONSTRUCTIVELY*, MAX.

WHAT--?!

GOOD LORD--!

19.

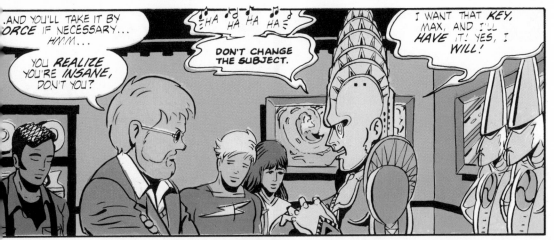

...AND YOU'LL TAKE IT BY FORCE IF NECESSARY... HMM...

YOU REALIZE YOU'RE INSANE, DON'T YOU?

♪ HA HA HA HA ♪

DON'T CHANGE THE SUBJECT.

I WANT THAT KEY, MAX, AND I'LL HAVE IT! YES, I WILL!

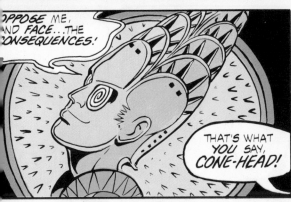

OPPOSE ME, AND FACE...THE CONSEQUENCES!

THAT'S WHAT YOU SAY, CONE-HEAD!

EAT FLAMING DEATH, YOU FASCIST PIG!

BUTCH, NO! THE HEAT-BEAM ISN'T THAT STRONG!

AAK! THE FORCE-FIELD!

SIGH ...FIELD'S NO GOOD, NOW, HE'S GRABBED YOU...IT WON'T STOP HIM FROM GRABBING YOU IF HE'S ALREADY GRABBED YOU...

THE ALARM!

VRREEP! VRRE EP!

VRREEP!-VRREEP!-VRE

BUT, I'M RIGHT HERE, BUTCH... I KNOW YOU'RE IN TROUBLE...

PLEASE, MR. DEKKER! I KNOW HE'S A JERK! BUT-- BUT--

HE'S MY ONLY BROTHER!

REALLY?! MY DEAR, I MUST SEE YOUR FAMILY TREE SOMETIME!

NOW, GIVE ME THE KEY... OR ELSE!

21.

ALRIGHT, DEKKO, YOU WIN! I--

♪

--OOOF!

I CONFESS!

'TWAS *I* WHAT DONE THE *DIRTY DEED!*

ZOT, MY FRIEND, I HAVE *BETRAYED* YOU!

ZOT! ARE YOU NOT *SHOCKED?!* YOUR *OWN FRIEND* IS THE *THIEF!!*

YEAH... SHOCKED.

HOW'D HE SWIPE IT FROM *ME??*

OH...

*NOW!* ISN'T ANYONE GOING TO ASK ME *WHY* I *COVET* THIS GLEAMING *BIBELOT?*

HUH?

ALL RIGHT, I'LL TELL YOU.

AS YOU KNOW *"THE DOORWAY AT THE EDGE OF THE UNIVERSE HAS BEEN IN EXISTENCE SINCE THE *DAWN OF TIME.*

BEFORE MAN EVER *FASHIONED* A DOOR OF HIS OWN..."THE DOOR" STOOD ALONE...

IT IS A PRODUCT OF *TECHNOLOGY*...YES, OF *TECHNOLOGY*...BUT, IT PREDATES *ALL* TECHNOLOGIES!

SO?

 ...SN'T IT *OBVIOUS*, YOU *LITTLE WORMS*?? DON'T YOU *SEE*?? TO OPEN THE DOOR SHALL SIGNAL THE *FINAL ASCENDANCY* OF MAN'S *PERFECT ART* AND THE *END* OF MAN'S *GREATEST FLAW: HIMSELF!* DON'T *GET* IT? HEH, HEH, YOU WILL...YOU WILL...

"THE MESSAGE IS CLEAR-- CULLED FROM THE *DIVINE DESIGN* BY MY *DESIGNER'S MIND!!* WHEN THE DOOR IS *FLUNG OPEN*, THE RACE WILL *DIE!* ALL SHALL PERISH BUT THE *GRAND MACHINE!*

"ONLY *I* SHALL REMAIN AS *PROPIGATOR* OF THE *MIRACLE*, AND AS ITS SOLE *LOVING WITNESS!*"

NOW YOU SEE...YOU SEE...

YEP. CRAZY AS A JAYBIRD...

HE'S GETTING AWAY!

 I'M SORRY I BECAME ABUSIVE JUST NOW... CALLING YOU WORMS... I WAS JUST SPEAKING *RELATIVELY*, YOU UNDERSTAND...

GOODBYE, NOW... GOODBYE...

N--NO--

 NO! I WON'T LET YOU! I WON'T!

STOP!! HE'LL K--!

AAAGH!!

IT SEEMS WE NEED TO MAKE AN *EXAMPLE*...

SOMEBODY, HELP, PLEASE...

I...I CAN'T *SEE*...!

PLEASE, DON'T DO THIS, ARTHUR!

OUT OF MY WAY, MAX! DON'T THINK I WON'T BROIL YOU, TOO!

PLEASE!

IF NOT FOR ME, THEN AT LEAST--!

SARAH...?

SARAH, WOULD YOU STOP...? PLEASE, STOP, SARAH...

?

STOP LOOKING AT ME...

PLEASE

S-57

STOP IT!!

STOP!!!

STOP!!

AND WITHIN THE MINUTE...

I REALLY THOUGHT WE WERE GONNA LOSE YOU, MAX...

SO DID I, ZACH... SO DID I...

2

TAIL 'EM, FLOYD!

SHORTLY...

ARE YOUR EYES BACK TO NORMAL, PRINCE?

YES, SIR... AND THANK YOU. I OWE YOU MY LIFE...

PAT! PAT!

YOU'LL BE UP AND AT 'EM IN NO TIME, DRU!

ZOT'S RIGHT, PRINCE! YOU'LL SEE...

OH, BUT HOW CAN WE EVER HOPE TO FIND THE KEY NOW! I'LL BE A LAUGHING STOCK!

DON'T WORRY, PRINCE. I'VE GOT MY ROBOT, FLOYD, TRACKING DEKKO RIGHT NOW, AND--

YOU!!

YOU WERE THE ONE WHO STOLE IT IN THE FIRST PLACE! NOW, YOU'RE GOING TO HELP US?? HELP US DO WHAT?? FIND IT FOR YOU??!

H-HEH...

NOW, LET'S NOT GET--

OU'LL PAY FOR THIS!

HOLD IT!

UH, LOOK... I KNOW THERE'S NO WAY I CAN MAKE YOU UNDERSTAND THE REASONS FOR WHAT I'VE DONE, SO I'LL JUST SAY THIS: I'VE GOT THE TRACKER: I CAN FIND THE KEY.

IF YOU WANT THE KEY TOO, THEN MAYBE YOU OUGHT TO TREAT ME WITH A LITTLE COURTESY.

"COURTESY"??

COURTESY.

GRRRRRRR

I OUGHTA PUNCH YOU RIGHT IN THE MOUTH IS WHAT I OUGHTA DO...

SIGH

25.

GOOD! REMIND ME TO PICK-UP A MATE FOR PHOEBE, MY *PET PENGUIN!*

POLE-POLICE HERE! WE GOT YOUR MESSAGE, ZOT!

WE'RE NEARING MR. DEKKER'S *LAND-PURCHASE* NOW!

I THINK IT'S JUST THE OTHER SIDE OF THIS *MOUNTAIN* UP AHEAD!

WELL, THERE'S ONE WAY TO *FIND OUT!*

27.

SOON, ON THE **MOUNTAIN SLOPES** OPPOSITE CASTLE DEKKO, AN ARTIFICIAL "**WARM-FIELD**" IS QUICKLY CONSTRUCTED, ELECTRIC PARKAS HANDED OUT AND A STRATEGY SESSION BEGINS...

I'VE SIGNALLED THE **INTERNATIONAL GUARD** FOR HELP! MR. DEKKER MAY BE THE **LAWFUL OWNER** OF THIS LAND, BUT THAT DOESN'T ENTITLE HIM TO **THIS** KIND OF DEFENSE!

YOU MAY FIND THAT EVEN THE **GUARD** MAY NOT BE ENOUGH TO STOP **DEKKER**, CAPTAIN LE ROSE.

C'MON, CAP'N! WE CAN **LICK 'IM!** WE DON'T NEED **HELP!**

**PIPE DOWN,** HOLIWISKI!

**SOUTH POLE,** HUH? SO, WHERE'S THE **PENGUINS?**

SORRY, MY CREW IS A BIT **BATTLE-HAPPY** TONIGHT. WE DON'T SEE MUCH **ACTION** IN THESE PARTS. A THREAT LIKE **DEKKER** IS A REAL **WINDFALL** TO A BORED **POLE-COP!**

I DUNNO IF YOU'LL FEEL AS **LUCKY** WHEN YOU MEET "DEKKO" **FACE-TO-FACE,** CAPTAIN!

WE WANT TO AVOID THAT, IF **POSSIBLE,** ZACH.

ARTHUR DEKKER IS A BIT OUT OF THE **POLE-POLICE'S** LEAGUE. ONLY THE **GUARD** HAS A CHANCE IN A **FULL-SCALE ASSAULT.**

HOPE YOU'LL LET **ME** HELP, AT LEAST, MAX.

OH, SURE...

WHAT ARE WE AFTER DEKKO **FOR,** ZOT?

A **NUMBER** OF THINGS, CAPTAIN! SOME COUNTS OF **ATTEMPTED MURDER,** FOR INSTANCE...ALSO, TO GET BACK THE "**KEY TO THE DOORWAY AT THE EDGE OF THE UNIVERSE**"!

DON'T WANDER TOO FAR FROM THE **HEATERS,** BUTCH.

YEAH, YEAH...

JUST AS IMPORTANT IS THAT WE GET HIM **PUT AWAY** AND **SOON!** THIS GUY IS **BONKERS! RIGHT,** MAX?

?

"**BONKERS**" JUST ABOUT **SAYS** IT, YES...

ARTHUR AND I WERE **FRIENDS** BEFORE A RARE CANCER MADE **BIONIC REPLACEMENTS** NECESSARY OVER HIS ENTIRE BODY. I SHOULD'VE **GUESSED** THAT SOONER OR LATER IT WOULD DRIVE HIM MAD. YOU **SEE,** CAPTAIN--

**HEY,** YOU GUYS, **C'MERE!** LOOK WHAT **I** FOUND!

3

LOOKS LIKE THIS **SHAFT** GOES DOWN TO **SEA-LEVEL!** IT'S BOUND TO **CONNECT** WITH THE **CASTLE CORRIDORS.**

HOW 'BOUT IT, MAX?

WELL, I SUPPOSE IT'S AS GOOD A PLAN AS **ANY.** ARTHUR WON'T BE EXPECTING **THIS** KIND OF ASSAULT!

**LUCKY FIND,** HUH?

**SHUCKS,** IT WUZ **NOTHIN'!**

I CAN LEND YOU A COUPLE OF MY PEOPLE AS **BACK-UP,** ZOT.

**THIS** TIME, WE **SHALL NOT** FAIL TO RECOVER THE **SACRED KEY!**

LET **ME** COME, ZACH.

**SORRY,** VIC. THIS IS TOO **DANGEROUS** FOR SOMEONE WITHOUT ANY **COMBAT EXPERIENCE.**

HEY, **C'MON!** THIS GADGET MAKES ME **INVISIBLE** TO ANY **ELECTRONIC SENSORS,** REMEMBER? IT HELPED ME **FILCH** THE KEY IN THE **FIRST PLACE!** I'M **SURE** I CAN GET IT BACK **NOW...**

WHAT?!

NO!!

Y-YU-C-CA-CAH≷ SPUTTER! ≷ YOU **CAN'T** LET **HIM** AT IT **AGAIN!!** HE'LL ONLY STEAL IT FOR **HIMSELF!**

≷sigh≷

I **DUNNO,** DRUFUS...HE **DOES** HAVE A POINT.

WE CAN **USE** HIM AND HE'S GOING TO HAVE TO STAY WITH THE **GROUP,** RIGHT? JUST KEEP AN **EYE** ON HIM IF YOU'RE SO NERVOUS.

**ME,** I'M GONNA TRUST VIC TO DO AS HE **SAYS.**

LET'S **GO,** HUH?

HEY, MING!

I STILL SAY YOU EJECTED FIRST!

AAAH, KEEP DREAMING, MULROY--

--YA CHICKEN!

KNOCK IT OFF, YOU TWO!

REAL SPIRITED BUNCH YOU GOT THERE, CAPTAIN!

"SPIRITED"? ≋Groan!≋ "FANATIC" IS MORE LIKE IT! THERE'S AN OFFICER FROM EACH COUNTRY HERE AND THEY'VE ALL GOT THE "HOMELAND'S HONOR" TO UPHOLD!

I'VE NEVER SEEN SUCH COMPETITIVE DRIVE IN MY LIFE!

STILL, IT IS INSPIRING SOMETIMES TO...

CLIK!

?

YES?

SOMETHING WRONG, CAPTAIN?

AND SOON...

NO GUARD-ROBOTS IN SIGHT! LET'S GET MOVING!

5

TO THINK HE BUILT THIS WHOLE PALACE FOR *HIMSELF*, WITH NO ONE TO EVEN *SHARE* IT!

NO FRIENDS, NO ONE TO TALK TO... WHO *WOULDN'T* GO MAD, HERE?

AH, THE STENCH OF *EVIL* IS ABOUT THIS PLACE!

ACTUALLY, I THINK THAT'S *AIR-FRESHENER*.

*GRRR!*

NEVER MIND.

*PEABODY!* ANY SIGN OF THAT *KEY?!*

NO NEED TO *SHOUT*, ZACHARY. I SHALL INFORM YOU OF ANY TRACE OF THE KEY'S *UNIQUE RADIATION*.

O.K., YOU *DO* THAT! I'VE GOT A HUNCH THAT IF WE FIND THE KEY, WE FIND *DEKKO, TOO!*

IN THE *MEANTIME*, LET'S TRY TO *KEEP MOVING* UNTIL WE TURN UP A *LEAD* OF SOME SORT! CAN'T HURT TO COVER AS MUCH GROUND AS *POSSIBLE*.

LET'S SEE WHAT'S AROUND THIS *CORNER!*

WH--! WH--! WHOA!!

GREETINGS, SUCKER.

NOT *THESE* BOTS AGAIN! THEY ALMOST *CREAMED* US *LAST* TIME!

CLIK! CLIK! CLIK! CLIK! CLIK!

O.K., GUYS! KEEP FIRING AND KEEP *MOVING*!!

BOOM BLAM BOOM

WE'VE GOT TO GET *BEYOND* THESE *RUST-BUCKETS*!

AIM FOR THE *KNEES*! I JUST *SNAPPED* ONE THAT WAY!

RIGHT!

THERE! GOT ONE!

HEY, *I* GOT *THAT* ONE!

THEY'RE *GAINING* ON US! *QUICKLY*, GUYS, THROUGH *HERE*!

DRUFUS! C'MON!

HUMANS AREN'T NEARLY *TIDY* ENOUGH TO DWELL WITHIN... NO, NOT *NEARLY*..

IT'S A *PRISTINE PLACE*, THIS *PRETTY PALACE* OF MINE...

I DON'T *WANT* YOU HERE, BUT HOW TO GET *RID* OF YOU... *THAT'S* A PROBLEM...

AH... MAX, MAX, MAX...

YOU REALLY *SHOULDN'T* HAVE COME!

NATURALLY, I COULD *ANNIHILATE* YOU ALL-- HA! HA! HA!--BUT *NO.* THAT WOULD BRING *OTHERS*...

I COULD LET YOU *GO*-- BUT YOU'D ONLY *RETURN* IN SEARCH OF THIS *PRECIOUS TRINKET*...

I DIDN'T COME HERE FOR THE *KEY*, ARTHUR. I CAME TO HELP *STOP* YOU FROM HARMING ANY MORE *PEOPLE!*

NOW, DON'T GET ALL *ALTRUISTIC* ON ME, MAX...

*EVERYBODY* WANTS *SOMETHING!* THE DOCTORS WHO *TRANSFORMED* ME, FOR EXAMPLE... ALL *THEY* WANTED WAS TO SQUEEZE AS MUCH AS THEY *COULD* FROM ME IN *MEDICAL BILLS*.

IF ONLY THEY KNEW WHAT A *FAVOR* THEY BESTOWED BY GIVING ME THE *ENLIGHTENED PERSPECTIVE* OF THE *CYBERNETIC ORGANISM* I AM TODAY!

BUT WE WANT TO HELP YOU, *TOO*, MR. DEKKER!

"MR. DEKKER" *INDEED*...

NO NEED TO STAND ON *FORMALITIES*... ESPECIALLY FOR *YOU*...

...SARAH...

*"SARAH"??*

BUT--!

SARAH WAS THE NAME OF HIS *LOVER* FROM *YEARS BACK!* THE ONE IN THE *PAINTING!*

MAX SAID SHE LEFT ARTHUR WHEN HE WAS STILL *HALF-HUMAN!* WHY WOULD--

JENNY, LISTEN *CLOSELY:* I WANT YOU TO REPEAT EVERYTHING I SAY...

"DON'T YOU REMEMBER..."

--REMEMBER, ARTHUR, HOW WE PLAYED LIKE KIDS IN THAT *OLD SHACK* WE FOUND? HOW WE'D RUN OUT IN THE *FIELDS* IN OUR *BARE FEET*...THEN LAY FOR HOURS IN THE TALL GRASS TILL AFTER DARK?

YOU SAID YOU DIDN'T *LIKE* THE CITY AS MUCH AS YOUR OLD HOME...BUT YOU LIKED ALL THE *PEOPLE*. IT WAS THE *PEOPLE* THAT BROUGHT YOU BACK *WASN'T IT?*

DON'T YOU *REMEMBER*, ARTHUR...?

9

WHOA!!

DON'T WORRY! *I'LL* GET HIM!

YOU MEAN *I'LL* GET HIM!!

GRA!

UH...

O.K! HE'S *YOUR'S!*

OH, NO! AFTER *YOU!*

*VIC!* HE CAN'T SEE *YOU!* GET OVER THERE AND OPEN THE *DOOR!*

THAT'S IT! NOW KEEP IT OPEN, TILL--?

CLIK!

*HEY!* WHAT ARE YOU *DOING?!*

*FRIEND ZOT!* THE SCOUNDREL IS *ESCAPING!*

*VIC!* COME BACK!

11

I *HATE* GRASS! IT MAKES ME *SICK* TO SEE IT SWAYING EVERY *WHICH-WAY*!

CAN'T THAT TRAMP, *MOTHER NATURE*, TEACH IT SOME *POSTURE*??

YOU LOVED *ALL* LIVING THINGS, ARTHUR! AS MUCH AS YOU LOVED *ME*!

"LOVE"?? HA!!

I *NEVER* LOVED YOU, YOU *MOPING MOP*!

OH? THEN I'M SURE IT WON'T MATTER--

OH? THEN I'M SURE--

--IT WON'T MATTER IF IF I STEP A LITTLE *CLOSER*.

OH, NO!

WHAT'S *WRONG*, MY LOVE?

DID YOU REALLY THINK THESE COULD *HOLD* ME?

OR DO YOU SHIVER--

--BECAUSE YOU REMEMBER HOW MY *HANDS* FEEL?

I DON'T *CARE*! STAY *AWAY*!

IT'S NOT TOO LATE TO START *AGAIN*, ARTHUR...

B-BUT, *YOU* KNOW I'M-- I'M NOT--

WHAT I LOVED IN YOU COULD *NEVER* BE REMOVED!

IT CAN STILL BE LIKE *BEFORE*!

...I CAN'T!

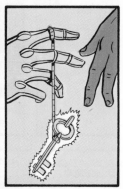

MAX...IS THAT *YOU*?

YES, ARTHUR, IT'S ME.

MAX...

...I'M SORR—*CLIK!*

HE'LL BE *OKAY*... THIS GADGET'LL JUST *FREEZE UP* HIS GEARS FOR A WHILE.

I'M AFRAID DRUFUS WAS *RIGHT*... I CAN'T LET YOU TAKE THIS KEY BACK.

WHEN YOU GET OUTSIDE, YOU'LL FIND ZACH'S CAR *MISSING*. I'M GOING TO DRIVE IT *BACK HOME* AND LEAVE IT AT *HIS* PLACE...I KNOW I DON'T HAVE A *LICENSE*, BUT I THINK I CAN *FLY* IT WELL ENOUGH...THE WAY THINGS STAND RIGHT NOW, IT'S MY ONLY *CHOICE*.

17

I'M GOING TO LEAVE *FLOYD* WITH YOU... HE HAS ALL THE *INFORMATION* ZACH WILL NEED TO *UNDERSTAND* WHY I'VE GOT TO DO THIS...

ZACH AND THE REST WILL BE HERE *SOON*. I'VE GOT TO GO...

*SHORTLY...*

BOOM!

*THERE* YA GO, ZOT! *I* GOT IT!

PTOOM!

*THANKS,* MING!

PTOOM!

*MAX!* WHAT ARE *YOU* DOING HERE?!

WHAT HAPPENED TO *DEKKO?*

I GOT IT *FIRST.*

*SEVERAL MINUTES LATER...*

WE'LL SEE TO IT THAT MR. DEKKER RECEIVES *PROPER TREATMENT.*

*I HOPE* SO... HE'LL NEED A LOT OF HELP...

ALMOST LOOKS AS IF HE'S SEEN A *GHOST*, DOESN'T HE?

A *GHOST?* YES, YOU MIGHT SAY THAT...

YOU MIGHT, INDEED...

MAX, WHAT DO YOU *MEAN?* SARAH'S STILL ALIVE...

*ISN'T* SHE?

*MAX...?*

I THINK IT'S ABOUT TIME TO *LEAVE...*

1

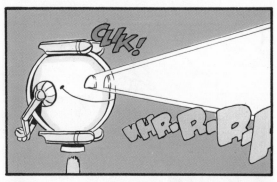

19

"HIGH COUNCILOR OF MILITARY AFFAIRS: *GENERAL HARCORT SHRAPP*."

TRADITIONALLY, WE HAVE BEEN *RIVALS* FOR POWER AND GAIN, BUT TODAY WE FIND A *COMMON GOAL*.

IN ORDER TO *STRENGTHEN* OUR *GRIP* ON THE WILL OF THE *POPULACE*, WE SIMPLY *MUST* HAVE A *WAR!*

"CHIEF SECRETARY OF THE RULING COMMITEE OF INTERNAL AND EXTERNAL FUNCTIONS AND OF THE BUREAU OF PREVIOUS AND PRESENT PARTY POLICIES:"

LET'S *CLARIFY* THAT...

"*SAM TWIK.*"

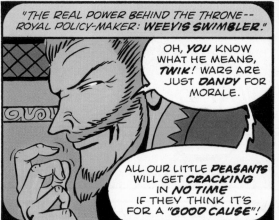

"THE REAL POWER BEHIND THE THRONE-- ROYAL POLICY-MAKER: *WEEVIS SWIMBLER.*"

OH, *YOU* KNOW WHAT HE MEANS, *TWIK!* WARS ARE JUST *DANDY* FOR MORALE.

ALL OUR LITTLE *PEASANTS* WILL GET *CRACKING* IN *NO TIME* IF THEY THINK IT'S FOR A *"GOOD CAUSE"!*

"THE CHURCH OF THE KEY'S GRAND INQUISITOR: *LUTHOR VON CLOKMANN.*"

BUT WHAT *TYPE* OF WAR? AND WITH *WHOM?*

A *HOLY* WAR.

WITH *EARTH.*

IT IS WRITTEN THAT A *GREAT MAN* SHALL OPEN THE *DOORWAY AT THE EDGE OF THE UNIVERSE* AND RETURN TO LEAD THE PEOPLE OF SIRIUS IV ON A *GREAT MISSION!*

THAT'S *IT!* THE *"GREAT MAN"* CAN BE ONE OF *US* AND THAT *"GREAT MISSION"* CAN BE--

--THE *COMPLETE ANNIHILATION OF PLANET EARTH.!!*

SOUNDS *PRACTICAL.*

AND *PROFITABLE!*

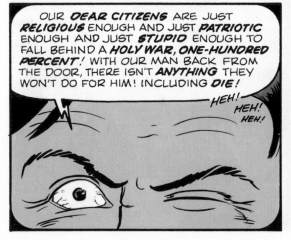

OUR *DEAR CITIZENS* ARE JUST *RELIGIOUS* ENOUGH AND JUST *PATRIOTIC* ENOUGH AND JUST *STUPID* ENOUGH TO FALL BEHIND A *HOLY WAR, ONE-HUNDRED PERCENT!* WITH OUR MAN BACK FROM THE DOOR, THERE ISN'T *ANYTHING* THEY WON'T DO FOR HIM! INCLUDING *DIE!*

HEH! HEH! HEH!

SO YOU SEE, I HAD TO STOP THEM AND NOW I CAN ONLY THINK OF ONE WAY TO *DO* THAT.

AS YOU WATCH THIS, I'M ON MY WAY *BACK* TO SIRIUS IV WITH THE KEY.

AND WHEN I *GET* THERE--

I'M GOING TO HOP ON THE FIRST SHUTTLE TO *"THE DOOR"* AND USE THE KEY TO OPEN IT *MYSELF!*

IT'S THE ONLY WAY I CAN THINK OF TO RUIN THEIR PLANS *FOR GOOD!* I HOPE YOU *UNDERSTAND*, ZACH...GOOD-BYE...

GET THE LIGHTS, PEABODY.

HE'S GOING TO *OPEN* IT! THAT'S *SACRILEGE!*

WE MUST *STOP* HIM! WE MUST STOP *ALL* OF IT!!

*Grrr!* I FEEL SO *STUPID!* AND --AND *USED!* I-I TR-TRUSTED *ALL* OF THEM! *ALL* OF THEM!!

MAYBE VIC IS *RIGHT*, DRUFUS. OPENING THE DOOR *WOULD* STOP THEM...

*NO!!* THERE'S GOT TO BE ANOTHER WAY! HE--HE--HE'S GOT NO *RIGHT!*

IT'S NOT *HIS!!*

GEEZ...THIS IS *KILLING* HIM.

I FEEL LIKE A *RAT.* I HAD THE KEY *MYSELF*, BEFORE,* AND I KEPT IT FROM DRUFUS, TOO!

*ISSUE #3 --SCOTT.

WE'VE GOT TO STOP *VIC!* THAT'S THE MOST *IMPORTANT* THING!

*PLEASE* COME BACK TO SIRIUS IV WITH ME, ZOT! HELP ME GET THE KEY BACK FROM VIC! WE CAN ALWAYS STOP THOSE VILLAINS *LATER!*

CHECK.

YAW

YOU *SEE?!* YOUR *UNCLE* AGREES!

THOSE DOGS *DON'T KNOW* WE'VE DISCOVERED THEIR PLAN *YET!* THEY'D THINK WE WERE *HELPING* THEM!

O.K., DRUFUS... I'LL DO IT...

HMM...WELL, JENNY... SIRIUS IV ISN'T EXACTLY A GREAT *VACATION* SPOT--

--BUT IN THE COMPANY OF A *"GOOD-WILL AMBASSADOR"*--

SOUNDS *GREAT!* WHEN DO WE LEAVE?

21

IT IS TWO DAYS LATER, AFTER TWENTY-NINE HOURS IN SPACE, THAT THE MARIANNE II (FLAGSHIP OF THE GIL-GANZ LUXURY LINE) PASSES SIRIUS III AND NEARS ITS DESTINATION...

--SO I LOOKED UP AT HIM AND SAID "GEE, MISTER, I DON'T NEED ANY PILLS. I'VE GOT DIPLOMATIC IMMUNITY!"

HA! HA!

HA! HA!

HA! HA!

HA! HA!

WILL THAT BE ALL, SIR?

BOY, EVEN AT SIX YEARS OLD, YOU HAD SOME CRAZY MIND, MAX!

HOW INTERESTING, THOUGH, TO THINK THAT ZOT'S PARENTS AND YOURSELF ORIGINALLY CAME FROM MY OWN PLANET! PERHAPS WE SHARE SOME COMMON ROOTS, ZOT!

MORE CHERRIES, GARÇON!

MISS WEAVER, I DO HOPE YOU ARE ENJOYING THE UNLIMITED CREDIT MY UNCLE ARRANGED. I MUST SAY YOU LOOK LOVELY IN THAT DRESS!

WHY, THANK YOU, PRINCE! YOU'VE BEEN JUST A WONDERFUL HOST TO ALL OF US!

WELL, OF ALL MY PRINCELY DUTIES, THESE ARE CERTAINLY...

'NIGHT, MAX.

Uh, EXCUSE ME, PRINCE. I'VE, Ah...GOTTA RUN!

AND SOON, IN ZOT'S PRIVATE QUARTERS...

HOWDY, STRANGER! WHATCHA DOIN'?

NOTHING...

C'MON, ZOT... YOU'VE BEEN SO QUIET SINCE WE LEFT EARTH... IS SOMETHING WRONG?

I'D RATHER NOT TALK ABOUT IT.

Y'KNOW, SOMETIMES, IT HURTS MORE TO TRY AN' KEEP THINGS INSIDE YOU...

SOMETIMES IT'S GOOD TO TALK THINGS OVER WITH A FRIEND... HOW ABOUT IT?

JENNY, I...

IT'S ABOUT YOUR **PARENTS**, ISN'T IT?

YOU'RE REMEMBERING THAT THEY WERE **BORN** ON SIRIUS?

I REALLY **DON'T LIKE** TO TALK ABOUT MY **PARENTS**, JENNY!

PLEASE, ZOT... I THINK I CAN **HELP**... MAYBE, IF YOU--

MAYBE IT'S **NONE OF YOUR DAMN BUSINESS!**

JUST LEAVE ME **ALONE**...

O.K., FINE BY ME... NO SKIN OFF **MY** TEETH...

GO AHEAD AND FEEL **SORRY** FOR YOURSELF... KEEP IT ALL CRAMMED AWAY... IT'S NOT LIKE YOU'RE HURTING ANYONE BUT **YOURSELF.** I JUST THOUGHT YOU WERE **SMARTER**, THAT'S ALL.

DO WHAT YOU **LIKE,** ZOT. **I** DON'T CARE...

**WAIT,** PLEASE...

I KNOW THAT YOU **DO**...

...AND MAYBE YOU'RE RIGHT ABOUT ME... MAYBE IT **IS** TIME I TALKED TO SOMEONE... ARE YOU STILL **INTERESTED?**

*Sniff!* COULD BE...

LET'S SIT DOWN...

"*I* WAS A **HAPPY** KID. NEVER **COMPLAINED** MUCH. NEVER REALLY **RESENTED** LIFE LIKE SOME CHILDREN..."

"I THOUGHT MY PARENTS WERE HAPPY WITH ME, **TOO.** SURE **SEEMED** THAT WAY..."

HE'S GOT YOUR **NOSE,** ALRIGHT!

AND **YOUR EYES!**

HEE! HEE! GNAAH!

"THOSE WERE **GOOD DAYS**..."

"DAD WAS A REAL **SOFTIE.** ALWAYS HAD TIME FOR ME, NO MATTER HOW **BUSY** HE WAS..."

TOBY LOOKS OKAY TO **ME,** ZACH...

YEAH, BUT **NO!** Y'SEE? HE'S GOT A FEVER! **LOOK!** HE'S REAL **PALE** AND...

"MOM GOT THE **HARD PART:** KEEPING ME **IN LINE.** BUT SHE DID IT **MASTERFULLY.** NEVER HAD TO SAY A THING. **ONE** LOOK WAS **ENOUGH**..."

HEY, **I** DIDN'T TAKE NOTHING...

I WAS JUST-- JUST WALKING **THROUGH**... I-- AW, **HECK**...

"AND WHEN **SHE** WAS AWAY THERE WAS ALWAYS PEABODY... AND HE WAS EVEN **HARDER** TO GET PAST."

"AT FIRST, I DIDN'T NOTICE HOW THEY WERE LEAVING ME WITH PEABODY MORE AND MORE **OFTEN**...

"I THOUGHT IT WAS JUST PART OF **GROWING UP**...

"IT WASN'T..."

"ONE DAY THEY WERE HAVING AN **UNUSUALLY SERIOUS DISCUSSION**...

"I WANTED MORE **ATTENTION**.

"I GUESS I PUSHED MY LUCK A LITTLE **TOO FAR**...

**SLAP!**

ZACH, I'M SORRY...I SHOULDN'T HAVE DONE THAT...

—Sniff—

YOU NEVER HIT ME **BEFORE**...

I **HATE** YOU!

"THE NEXT MORNING, THEY LEFT ON A **SHORT VACATION** WHICH DIDN'T INCLUDE ME.

"I WOULDN'T SAY **GOOD-BYE**.

"OF COURSE, ALL WAS **FORGIVEN** BY THE FIRST **PHONE-CALL**.

HOW'RE YOU HOLDING UP, ZACH?

GREAT! DIDJA **BUY** ME ANYTHING?

"WE'D TALK FOR **HOURS**...

"BUT THE CALLS GREW **SHORTER** AS THE VACATION GREW **LONGER**...

NOT **ANOTHER** WEEK, DAD! COME HOME, **NOW**!

I'M **SORRY**, ZACH. WE...WE **CAN'T**...

"AND THE CALLS **STOPPED**."

25

"UNCLE MAX LET ME VISIT AS MUCH AS I WANTED, BUT HE TOLD ME I COULDN'T MOVE IN..."

RAHR!

HM- DUM-DE DUM...

"HE SAID *THAT* WOULD BE GIVING UP HOPE."

"HE WAS A GREAT TEACHER..."

NOW, D'Y'SEE WHY THIS STORY IS EVEN MORE FUN AS A BOOK THAN ON THE *VID*?

HA! HA! YEAH!

"I STARTED TO IMPROVE REAL FAST IN SCHOOL..."

WOW...

"...IN SPORTS..."

WOW!

"...AND BEST OF ALL..."

WOW!!

"I BECAME WORLD ARCADE-MARKSMAN CHAMPION--AT NINE!"

"I MADE AS MANY FRIENDS AS POSSIBLE... SOMETHING--I DON'T KNOW WHAT--DROVE ME LIKE CRAZY TO ALWAYS BE ON TOP..."

"I WAS ON A BUSY RIVER CROSSWALK ONE DAY WITH PEABODY WHEN IT HAPPENED..."

"A FLYER HAD GONE OUT OF CONTROL..."

IT'S GOING TO **HIT** US!!

"A POLICEMAN AND HIS GUN WERE NEAR.

HUH?!

B'ZAP!

"I KNEW WHERE TO AIM--

CHOK!

"-- SO THAT ONLY ONE ENGINE MALFUNCTIONED. THE FLYER'S COURSE WAS ALTERED...

FLASH

"IT LANDED IN THE RIVER...

"AND, AS LONG AS I WAS A GOOD SWIMMER, WELL, WHY NOT HELP WITH THE REST...?

I'VE GOT YOU, SIR.

"IT ALL SEEMED PRETTY REASONABLE TO ME AT THE TIME. BUT WHEN THE REPORTERS CAME--

"-- I WAS AN INSTANT STAR! THE MEDIA GOT A HOLD OF MY NICKNAME AND I WAS OFFICIALLY 'ZOT'! I WAS TEN YEARS OLD AT THE TIME..."

AND, ON THE **LIGHTER** SIDE...

"I STUMBLED INTO A FEW MORE LUCKY RESCUES AFTER THAT. IT BEGAN TO SEEM LIKE BEING A HERO WAS JUST NATURAL FOR ME.

"MAX WENT ALONG WITH IT. HE DESIGNED MY BOOT-JETS AND ALL THE OTHER GADGETS. I MADE MYSELF A COSTUME...

"SO...

"I'M A HERO NOW...

"KNOWN TO MILLIONS..."

27

...AND JUST ANOTHER *ABANDONED* KID.

IS *THAT* WHAT YOU THINK, ZOT? YOU THINK THEY JUST *ABANDONED* YOU?

C'MON, JEN. WHAT DOES IT SOUND LIKE TO *YOU?*

IT SOUNDS LIKE THERE'S *GOT* TO BE ANOTHER EXPLANATION...

YOU'VE HELPED ME A LOT, ZOT-- GIVEN ME A KIND OF *HOPE.* I'D LIKE TO GIVE SOME OF IT *BACK...* IF I *CAN...*

ATTENTION ALL PASSENGERS: NOW APPROACHING *SIRIUS IV...* I *REPEAT:* NOW APPROACHING *SIRIUS IV...*

PAY ATTENTION, BUTCH. THIS IS *SERIOUS*...

ZARB, THIS IS MR. *RAYMOND TAYLOR*. HIS SON IS *VIC* TAYLOR, THE GUY WHO, UM...TOOK THE *KEY*!

I'M SURE ZOT CAN *HELP*, UNCLE ZARBIM...

YEAH, YEAH... I *KNOW* WHERE WE ARE...

GENERAL, I WISH TO CONVEY MY *SINCEREST APOLOGIES* FOR THE *DISGRACEFUL BEHAVIOR* OF MY SON, *VICTOR*.

I INTEND TO TAKE *FULL RESPONSIBILITY* FOR THE BOY'S ACTIONS.

'COURSE, IT'S NOT REALLY *MR. TAYLOR'S* FAULT...

*ZOT* MAY THINK THAT, SIR, BUT AS A *PARENT*, I CAN'T HELP FEELING *TO BLAME* SOMEHOW FOR WHAT VIC HAS DONE.

I JUST HOPE THIS WHOLE UGLY AFFAIR CAN BE *SETTLED* SOON...

*INDEED*, SIR. LET US "*HOPE*."

A MILD *DRIZZLE* BEGINS TO FALL AS A *SHORT MOTORCADE* RUMBLES SLOWLY THROUGH *SIRIUS IV'S* DENSE CAPITOL CITY...

THESE *CROWDS* DON'T SEEM TOO *EXCITED* TO SEE US, ZOT...

OH, THEY'RE ONLY HERE 'CAUSE THEY WERE *TOLD* TO COME.

SIRIUS IV IS KIND OF *OPPRESSIVE*... NOBODY EVER DOES ANYTHING HERE BECAUSE THEY *WANT* TO...:

2

NOT MUCH *FREEDOM*, HUH?

I'LL SAY! IT'S ALL *RULES* AND *STATUTES* AND *REGULATIONS*... NOBODY REALLY KNOWS WHAT THEY'RE DOING, JUST WHAT THEY'RE *TOLD* TO DO...

LOTTA *APATHY, PETTY-MINDEDNESS, LAZINESS*...

Y'KNOW, THERE ARE PLACES ON *MY* WORLD THAT ARE A LOT LIKE THAT...

REALLY, JENNY?

YEAH, THEY'RE CALLED *"POST OFFICES."* *

YAY! YAY! YAY! YAY!

YAY! YAY...

YOU SAY THIS *"ZOT"*-BOY IS A *FRIEND* OF THE *THIEF*??

Y-YES, UNCLE.

THEN HOW CAN YOU SERIOUSLY EXPECT HIM TO HELP US *RETRIEVE* THE KEY?

WELL?? ( WAVE LIKE YOU *MEAN* IT.)

I...I'M SURE ZOT WILL HELP US, UNCLE...

HEY, THERE, PEABODY! BETCHA DIDN'T *KNOW* I WAS A *CELEBRITY!*

CORRECT: I DID NOT KNOW THAT...

I TELL YOU, MAX, WHEN I GET MY *HANDS* ON THAT *SON OF MINE*--!

DON'T JUDGE VIC TOO HARSHLY JUST *YET*, RAYMOND... HE'S GOT SOME *PRETTY SOUND REASONS* TO HOLD ON TO THAT KEY!

WE'LL GIVE YOU THE *FULL RUNDOWN* TONIGHT.

3

THE OPINIONS EXPRESSED HEREIN ARE THOSE OF THE CHARACTERS AND DO NOT NECESSARILY REFLECT THE VIEWS OF THE AUTHOR, EDITORS OR ECLIPSE PUBLISHING. IF YOU OR SOMEONE YOU KNOW IS AN EMPLOYEE OF THE UNITED STATES POSTAL SERVICE, I'M SURE YOU/HE/SHE ARE/IS A NICE, HARD-WORKING, RESPONSIBLE PERSON. NO, *REALLY,* I MEAN IT. HONEST.(PLEASE DON'T DO ANYTHING RASH...) —SCOTT

GOOD CITIZENS OF *SIRIUS IV*! I, YOUR PRINCE, HAVE RETURNED FROM THE DISTANT PLANET *EARTH*, WHERE MY COMPANIONS AND I DISCOVERED SOME *VITAL INFORMATION*...

...INFORMATION THAT WILL HELP US *RETRIEVE* OUR BELOVED *"KEY TO THE DOORWAY AT THE EDGE OF THE UNIVERSE!*

ASSISTING ME IN MY QUEST WAS A *YOUNG HERO* WHOSE VALOR AND COURAGE IS *UNSURPASSED* ON HIS WORLD!

WOULD YOU ALL NOW GIVE A *WARM* AND *ENTHUSIASTIC WELCOME* TO EARTH'S *GREATEST CHAMPION*--

APPLAUSE

--ZOT!

CLAP CLAP CLAP CLAP CLAP

THANK YOU, UH...

SCRATCH

IT'S NICE OF YOU TO *HAVE* ME HERE AND ALL...

I'LL CERTAINLY DO MY *BEST* IN TRYING TO HELP YOU FIND THE KEY. I CAN'T MAKE ANY *PROMISES*, BUT I'M SURE IT'LL ALL WORK OUT...

UH...THANKS AGAIN...

CLAP CLAP CLAP CLAP

IS THAT *ALL?*

ALL RISE NOW FOR THE *WORLD ANTHEM.*

*THE AUDIENCE STANDS AS ONE AT THESE WORDS.*

AND IN ALL PARTS OF THE IMMENSE HALL--

--THEY BEGIN TO PLAY IN *PERFECT SYNCHRONIZATION* AND *HARMONY...* AND A *CHANGE* OCCURS IN THE FACES OF THE PLAYERS...

"ONLY A MINUTE AGO THEY WERE ALL SO *LIFELESS* AND *UNCARING...*"

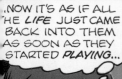

...NOW IT'S AS IF ALL THE *LIFE* JUST CAME BACK INTO THEM AS SOON AS THEY STARTED *PLAYING...*

"WHAT ARE THEY *THINKING ABOUT?*"

HEY...*THIS* IS THE TUNE THAT *MAX* TAUGHT ME THE OTHER DAY... HE SAID IT WAS *HUNDREDS OF YEARS* OLD. I WONDER...

WAS SIRIUS *ALWAYS* LIKE THIS...?

?

5

THE NEXT DAY...

DRAT! WHERE DID THAT BUG GET TO?

OH, WELL... I DOUBT THEY WERE DISCUSSING ANYTHING VITAL...

FATHER, I HAVE BROUGHT YOU THE HERO OF WHOM I HAVE OFTEN SPOKEN! THE ONE CALLED ZOT!

I AM TRULY HONORED, YOUR MAJESTY.

YES, YES, OF COURSE...

SO, EARTHLING, WHAT MANNER OF ASSISTANCE DO YOU OFFER MY PEOPLE?

ONLY MY SKILLS AND SOME KNOWLEDGE OF THE THIEF'S WAYS, YOUR MAJESTY...

ZOT KNOWS THE THIEF PERSONALLY, FATHER.

THOUGH HE ASSURES ME THIS WILL NOT MAKE HIM BIASED.

HMM...OR SO HE SAYS...

STILL, HE IS AN EARTHLING LIKE HIS FRIEND.

CAN WE AFFORD TO TRUST AN OUTWORLDER IN MATTERS SUCH AS THIS?

A FRIEND OF THE THIEF, YOU SAY... AND A MERE BOY, AT THAT!

YOUR MAJESTY--

YES, WEEVIS, WHAT IS IT?

PERHAPS IF A TRUSTED MEMBER OF THE ROYAL FAMILY WERE TO BE SENT AS ESCORT FOR THESE BOYS...

PSST, PSST PSST...

HMM...

I COULD JUST SCREAM, WATCHING THAT SNAKE TELL MY FATHER WHAT TO DO...

DRUFUS, I BELIEVE I SHALL SEND YOUR UNCLE ZARBIM TO ACT AS YOUR ESCORT.

A WISE CHOICE.

PERHAPS HE CAN HELP PREVENT ANOTHER DISGRACEFUL FAILURE OF THE SORT YOU SUFFERED ON EARTH -- AND FOR WHICH I AM SEVERELY DISAPPOINTED IN YOU!

Y-YES, FATHER.

THIS TIME I EXPECT RESULTS!

ONE OF THESE FINE DAYS, I MAY NOT BE AROUND TO GUIDE YOUR EVERY STEP.

I EXPECT YOU TO BE FULLY PREPARED FOR THAT DAY! AM I MAKING MYSELF CLEAR?

Y-YES, FATHER.

7

DON'T BE *DOWNCAST*, MY GOOD PRINCE. *I* HAVE FAITH IN YOU...

I'M SURE YOU CAN HELP FIND THE KEY FOR *ME*--

AH, ≳EH-HEH!≲, THAT IS, FOR *US*...EH... I MEAN FOR THE GOOD OF ALL CONSP-- *CONCERNED* ≳EH-HEH!≲ Uh--

HMM...

DRUFUS, YOU ARE *EXCUSED.*

THANK YOU, FATHER...

*HA!* THE RAT IS CAUGHT IN HIS *OWN TRAP!*

NOT *YOU*, WEEVIS...STAY *RIGHT HERE.*

Uh-Oh...

*D*ON'T BE FOOLED, DEAR READER...THE KING IS NOT THE *ONLY* RULING POWER ON SIRIUS IV! THAT NIGHT, A *SECRET MEETING* IS HELD...

*BAH!* WHAT *DIFFERENCE* DOES IT MAKE IF THE KING *SUSPECTS* YOU, SWIMBLER?

ONCE THE KEY IS *RETRIEVED*, WE'LL SEND OUR MAN THROUGH *"THE DOOR"*, HE'LL COME OUT, LEAD A *HOLY WAR* AGAINST EARTH AND WE'LL HAVE THE KING *AND* THE PEOPLE RIGHT WHERE WE *WANT* THEM!

DO NOT *UNDERESTIMATE* THE KING, *GENERAL SHRAPP!* I TELL YOU, HE'S GOTTEN A LOT LESS *PLIABLE*, LATELY

IT'S *YOUR PROBLEM*, SWIMBLER. HOW DO YOU AIM TO *CORRECT* IT?

Hmm... *I KNOW!* LET'S *KILL* HIM!

HIS *ONLY SON*, DRUFUS WOULD BE LIKE *PUTTY* IN MY HANDS! YES...

BUT, *KILLING THE KING?* ≳TSK, TSK≲ MESSY, MESSY. I SAY *NAY.*

VON CLOKMANN?

HE CERTAINLY *DESERVES* IT. THE *SINNER...*

I SAY *AYE.*

UP TO ME, EH? HEH, HEH, HEH... OH, *WHY NOT?* I SAY *AYE!*

SO, BOYS--

--WHO GETS TO *DO* THE *DIRTY DEED?*

⑧

SOMEONE THE KING *HIMSELF* HAS EMPLOYED A FEW TIMES! HE'S AN *ESPECIALLY GOOD* SPY AND *ASSASSIN.* WE DON'T KNOW MUCH ABOUT HIM EXCEPT THAT HE'S ALWAYS *DELIVERED--*

*CLIK!*

--AND THAT HE'S CODE-DESIGNATED AS J9A9K...

...*OTHERWISE* KNOWN AS *9-JACK-9!*

*GOOD MORNING,* GENTLEMEN.

IT IS *EVENING,* MR. 9...

I AM ON *EARTH,* MR. TWIK...

WELL, *WHERE-EVER* YOU ARE, JACK, I'VE GOT A *JOB* FOR YOU! HOW WOULD YOU LIKE TO *OFF* THE *KING?*

HMM...

WE'LL PAY *HANDSOMELY,* MIND YOU! I'M PREPARED TO OFFER AS MUCH AS THE *OLD BOY* GAVE YOU FOR THAT *EARTH-JOB!*

THERE WERE *TWO* OF *THEM!*

YES, BUT I DID BOTH OF *THEM* AT THE *SAME TIME,* WEEVIS... WOULDN'T THINK THAT A GOOD SCALE FOR *COMPARISON...*

ALSO, *ROYAL JOBS* CAN BE A BIT *TRICKIER...*

OH, I'LL *DOUBLE* HIS FEE! *I'VE* HEARD OF THIS MAN... HE'S *WORTH* A FEW *SALARY CUTS.*

I'VE ALWAYS *SAID* MY SOLDIERS WOULD WORK FOR *NOTHING!*

*TWICE* THE FEE WILL BE *FINE...*

*EXCELLENT!*

HOW SOON CAN YOU GET HERE FROM *EARTH?*

OH, I CAN START *NOW,* IF YOU LIKE...

I'VE GOT SOME TIME TO KILL.

⑨

THE *"DOORWAY AT THE EDGE OF THE UNIVERSE"* HAS EXISTED SINCE THE *DAWN OF TIME!* BECAUSE THE DOOR IS OFFICIALLY IN *NEUTRAL SPACE*, ALL APPROACHES TO THE DOOR ARE UNDER *STRICT INTERSTELLAR CONTROL.*

SURROUNDING THE DOOR AT A RADIUS OF *1.5 KILOMETERS* IS AN AIR-FILLED, TRANSPARENT *SPHERE* WHICH IS CONNECTED TO THIS *SPACE STATION.*

THE VAST UNKNOWN

AIR-FILLED SPHERE

SPACE

SIRIUS IV

YOU ARE HERE

FINAL SCREENING AND DETECTION.

THE DOOR

EQUIPMENT CHAMBER.

SPACE STATION 88.BGO

ATMOSPHERIC CONDITIONING STATION.

THE ENDLESS COSMOS

THE FINAL FRONTIER

GOL-L-LY, BERBAX, THAT LADY SURE IS *BUILT* FUNNY!

WHADDYA THINK HER *MIDDLE* PART LOOKS LIKE, DALLIT?

MRMM...

DAWK!

FFN

ZZz

10

ARE THERE ANY *QUESTIONS?*

YES, MA'AM! ME AN' MAH FRIEND WERE A WONDERIN'...

≥Sigh≤

ALL SET, SIR. YOU MAY ENTER THE SPHERE.

≥ GMERK ≤

≥ DING ≤

≥ FB ≤

YOU KNOW, DRUFUS... I'VE BEEN *THINKING...* REMEMBER THAT *LITTLE MACHINE* VIC HAS THAT CAN MAKE HIM *INVISIBLE* TO ELECTRONIC *EYES* AND STUFF? WHAT IF THAT CAN ALSO CONCEAL THE KEY?

≥ Sigh...≤

AND WHAT IF VIC IS IN *DISGUISE* AGAIN AND--

OH, STOP *WORRYING,* BOY.

WE'LL FIND THE *SCOUNDREL!*

≥ Sigh...≤

HMM...

THERE'S A *SUSPICIOUS* ONE...

PEABODY! SEE IF YOU GET ANY READINGS ON THAT *WEIRD-LOOKING* GUY...

YOU'LL HAVE TO BE MORE *SPECIFIC,* ZACHARY.

THE ONE IN FRONT OF THE *OLD LADY...*

...

WELL?

ZACHARY... I DETECT NO "OLD LADY"

*SURE* YOU DO! SHE'S RIGHT *IN FRONT* OF Y-- HEY, WAIT A MINUTE...

IF VIC'S DEVICE MAKES HIM *INVISIBLE* TO MACHINES AND YOU CAN'T SEE--

*OF COURSE!*

*THAT'S HIM!!*

@%!!#

11

NNG!

YOU WISH!

MMF!!

CRASH!!

OFFICIAL BRONZE DOOR

I ♥

STOP!

HEY, YOU WRECK 'EM, YOU BUY 'EM!

≈GROAN..≈ TRY NOT TO HURT HIM, GUYS!

UH-OH!

THEY'RE GETTING CLOSE!

SOMEONE STOP HIM!!

YOU'RE UNDER ARREST!

SUPER DOUBLE MINGO!

HOLD THAT ELEVATOR, YOUNG MAN!

NO!! DON'T CLOSE THAT DOOR!

WHOOP!

JUST MADE IT, MA'AM.

GRRR!

⑬

SOON, IN THE HANGAR DECK BELOW--

YOUNG MAN! COULD YOU DO SOMETHING FOR ME?

SURE, LADY! NEED A *RIDE?*

YOU *GUESSED* IT!

≒ *UNNH!!* ≒

WHY DOES *SAVING THE EARTH* HAVE TO MAKE ME SUCH A *LOUSE?*

*THE ROYAL PALACE...*

IT RAINS *A LOT* HERE, DOESN'T IT, MAX?

*YUP.* ABOUT HALF OF SIRIUS GETS *TOO MUCH* RAIN AND THE *OTHER* HALF DOESN'T GET ANY AT ALL...

REAL *COMMITTEE EFFORT.*

YEAH--

--BUT EVEN IF IT WAS *SUNNY...* IT'D *STILL* BE *GLOOMY...*

SO MANY PEOPLE BEING FORCED TO KEEP SO MUCH HIDDEN.

MAX... DO YOU THINK ZOT'S PARENTS *DESERTED* HIM?

OH, NO. NO CHANCE OF *THAT*.

ZOT TOLD ME THAT *HE* THINKS THEY *DID*.

*WHAT?* BUT THAT'S *RUBBISH!*

I DON'T BELIEVE IT *EITHER*, BUT I CAN SEE WHY *HE* MIGHT...I MEAN, HE WAS AWFULLY *YOUNG* WHEN THEY LEFT...

HMM... WHAT DID YOU TELL HIM?

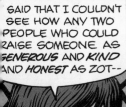

SAID THAT I COULDN'T SEE HOW ANY TWO PEOPLE WHO COULD RAISE SOMEONE AS *GENEROUS* AND *KIND* AND *HONEST* AS ZOT--

--COULD EVER DO SOMETHING AS *CRUEL* AS *DESERTING* THEIR TEN-YEAR-OLD SON. IT JUST DOESN'T ADD UP...

SURE *DOESN'T*. WHAT *ELSE* DID YOU SAY?

I ALSO TOLD HIM HE WAS BEING A JERK.

*HA!-HA!* RIGHT AGAIN! IF ZACH IS GOING TO GET *THAT* KIND OF ADVICE, I CAN RETIRE FROM THIS *UNCLE BUSINESS* IN NO TIME!

POOR KID...HE REALLY *IS* A JERK, SOMETIMES...

SO, I DID GOOD?

YOU DID GOOD, JENNY...

ZACH IS LUCKY TO KNOW YOU...

M̲EANWHILE, HIGH ABOVE THE SWIRLING STORMCLOUDS...

GIVE IT UP, VIC! YOU CAN'T KEEP THIS UP *FOREVER*...

MAYBE I CAN LOSE THEM IN THIS *CLOUDBANK*.

15

AND LOSE THEM HE DOES, BUT ONLY TEMPORARILY...

THERE'S HIS *SHIP*, GUYS! BUT WHAT'S THAT *BUILDING* HE'S LANDED ON?

WHILE INSIDE...

RAWR!!

WHAT *IS* THIS PLACE??

HYAK! HYAK!

BNUH

HAYDEN PLANETARIUM

BIG HAIRY LUMP

MUST BE SOME KIND OF *INDOOR ZOO...*

OH, NO! NOT YOU AGAIN!

RAWR!!

HYAK?

I'LL *NEVER* QUIT TILL YOU GIVE BACK THAT *KEY*, VIC!

YOU MIGHT THINK YOU'RE DOING EARTH SOME *GOOD*, VIC, BUT I'M TELLING YOU, THERE'S BEEN A HELLUVA LOT OF *BAD* THROWN IN SO FAR!

SO *WHAT?!!* *YOU* KNOW WHAT'S AT STAKE HERE!!

ARE YOU GONNA TELL ME ANY OF THIS STUFF IS MORE IMPORTANT THAN *AVOIDING A WAR?!*

I WANT TO AVOID IT, *TOO*, YOU JERK! BUT NOT *THIS* WAY!

*YEAH?* AND HOW'S *YOUR* WAY BETTER THAN *MINE?!* HAH? *TELL* ME ABOUT IT!

HERE, HERE...WHAT'S ALL *THIS* THEN? A FAMILY QUARREL?

AH, STAY *OUT* OF THIS!!

WHA-A-AT?

C'MON, CHIMP, BACK TO YOUR CAGE.

HEY!

YOU *MORONS*, HE'S *GETTING AWAY!*

"HE"?

HYAK! HYAK!

HYAK!

HELP! HELP! THEY WERE TRYING TO STEAL MY *PURSE!*

OH! SO *THAT'S* YOUR GAME--

YEOWW!

CRUNCH!

MY HAND!!

*DARN IT!* PEABODY CAN'T SEE VIC AND I DON'T WANT TO *HURT* ANYONE SO I GUESS IT'S UP TO--

ARRR

*APE-BOY TO THE RESCUE!*

DON'T LET HIM OUT OF YOUR *SIGHT*, BUTCH!

I'LL JOIN YOU AS SOON AS I'VE STRAIGHTENED THIS OUT.

17

18

--I *ASSURE* YOU, MY P-PRINCE, IF I'D ONLY *KNOWN*--

*C'MON*, GUYS! *FORGET* THEM! WE'VE STILL GOT TO CATCH *VIC!*

OKAY, BOZO.

CLIK!

YOU *ASKED* FOR IT!

*GIMME* THE KEY OR *FRY!*

BUTCH, *WAIT!* YOU DON'T *UNDERSTAND!*

DREED! DREEP! DREEP! DREEP! DREEP! DREEP! DREEP! DREEP!

WE'VE GOT TO FIND THE *HAT!* THE KEY IS IN THE HAT!!

*WHA*--?

*THERE IT IS!*

DON'T LET HIM *ESCAPE!*

DREEP! DREEP! DREEP!— DREEP! DREEP! DREEP!

*GET HIM,* BUTCH!! *GET HIM!*

I'M *TRYIN'!* I'M *TRYIN'!*

DREEP!— DREEP! DREEP! DREE DREEP! DREEP! DREEP!— DREEP! DREEP! DREEP! DREEP!— DREEP! DREEP! DREEP! DREEP! DREEP!

NOTHIN'??

I BEEN SWINDLED!

SHOOP!

HEY! LET ME OUTTA HERE!!

I'M A PERSON, YOU DODO!

C'MON! HOW MANY TALKING MONKEYS DO YOU KNOW?!

LET ME OUT!

LOOKS LIKE ANOTHER ROOKIE, HERB.

HE'LL LEARN, HE'LL LEARN...

MOMENTS LATER, A WEARY PRINCE DRUFUS EMERGES ON THE ROOF TO FIND--

HE'S GETTING AWAY!

BUT HOW DO I STOP HIM WHEN I CAN BARELY FLY A CAR!?

STILL, IF I TRY TO GET THE OTHERS IT MAY BE TOO LATE!!

WHAT WOULD FATHER SAY THEN??

≶BRRRR!≶

21

DUMB DRESS.

DUMB HAT...DUMB MASK...

JUST ANOTHER *DUMB IDEA* FROM DUMB OLD ME...

≈SIGH≈ NEXT TIME I PLAY HERO, MAYBE I'LL *TELL* SOMEONE ABOUT IT FIRST!

FLUP!

IT'D HELP TO KNOW WHAT *SIDE* I'M ON FOR A CHANGE.

OH, WELL--

--AT LEAST *THE CONSPIRACY* IS STILL MISSING THEIR *PRECIOUS KEY* AND, FOR NOW, TIME IS ON *MY SIDE.*

UH-OH.

MAYBE NOT.

COMPANY.

THAT'S *DRUFUS* BACK THERE!

NO CLOUDS LEFT TO *LOSE* HIM IN... LOOKS LIKE JUST *DESERT* DOWN THERE... IT FIGURES...

WHAT *ELSE* COULD GO WRONG?

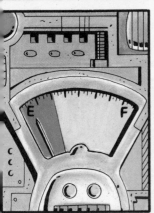

!

HEY, HE'S BEGINNING TO *SLOW!*

GREAT...

I'VE *CAUGHT UP* WITH HIM...

*NOW* WHAT DO I DO??

NO, I GUESS I ALREADY KNOW, BUT...

...SO FAR *DOWN.*

IF I *FAIL...*

HUH?

23

HOW LONG DO THEY EXPECT TO BE *SEARCHING?*

THE DESERT'S *BIG*, MR. TAYLOR...

OVER 200,000 SQUARE KILOMETERS OF *TRACKLESS WASTE!*

THE SEARCH MAY TAKE *TIME!*

WHAT DO YOU SAY TO *THAT*, BOY?

ANY MORE OF YOUR *WITTY* REMARKS FOR US?

NO, SIR... I'M NOT IN MUCH OF A *JOKING MOOD*, I GUESS...

THIS IS *SERIOUS BUSINESS.*

25

*THAT EVENING...*

SIRE, I MUST SAY IT'S A *DANDY* IDEA, SPENDING THE NIGHT IN YOUR *MONITOR ROOM!*

YES, YES... "*DANDY*"...

ALL IS IN *READINESS,* SIRE.

THIS WAY, YOU'LL BE THE *FIRST TO KNOW* WHEN YOUR SON IS FOUND!

≈SIGH≈

MY *ASSISTANT* IS JUST *TIDYING UP* A BIT, YOUR *MAJESTY...*

HE'LL BE *DONE* SOON.

IN YOU GO...

≈AHEM≈

I EXPECT YOU TO MAKE IT *QUICK,* MY GOOD MAN.

OH, I USUALLY *DO,* SIRE.

JACK!

WEEVIS, HELP ME!

THERE'S AN *ASSASSIN* IN HERE!

**NO!** **LET ME OUT!!**

*SLAM!*

THE END.

*WHY, JACK? WHY ME? HAVEN'T I ALWAYS PAID YOU WELL?!*

OH, YES; BUT NOW YOU SEE THE VALUE OF AN *EXCLUSIVE* CONTRACT...

JACK, *PLEASE...* I DON'T *WANT* TO D-DIE TONIGHT.

NOW, NOW...TAKE IT LIKE A *MAN*, SIRE! AFTER ALL, I DON'T THINK ANY OF THE HALF DOZEN PEOPLE *YOU* HAD ME KILL--

--WERE ANY *MORE* PREPARED TO GO!

*AAH!* HERE, YOU'RE *TENSE. NERVOUS...*

*SHUMP!*

LET ME *HELP* YOU.

YOU MAY FEEL A BIT *CONSTRAINED--*

*SNAP! SNAP!*

NO...

--BUT IT SHOULDN'T LAST *LONG...*

SO THERE'S NO NEED TO *STRUGGLE.*

THE END.

PERHAPS YOU FEEL A BIT *COLD?*

IT'LL PASS...

THE END.

EVEN A BIT SHORT OF *BREATH?*

BUT WHO NEEDS AIR?

WHOOPS! THERE GO THE LIGHTS!

OH, WELL...

THE

7

NEXT: IT'S ALWAYS DARKEST

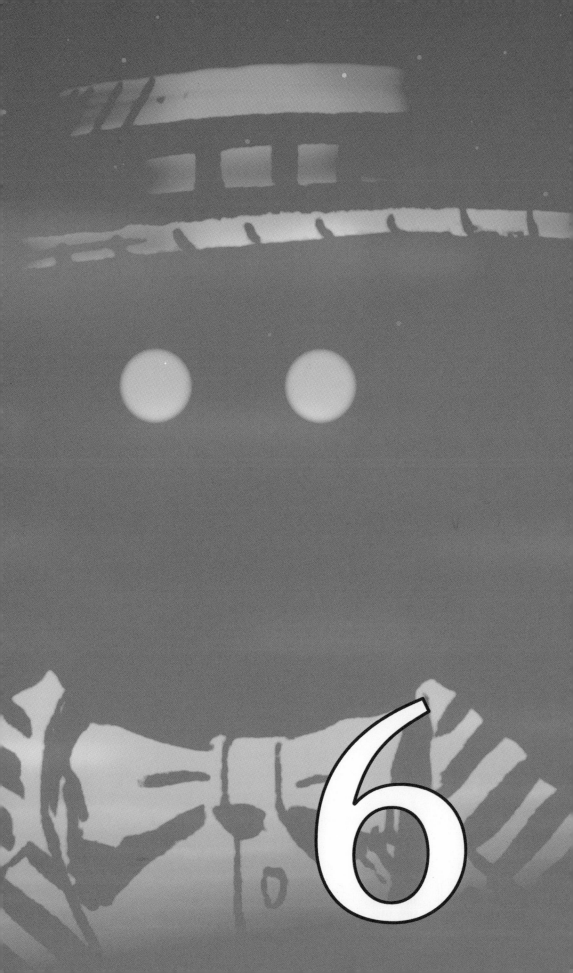

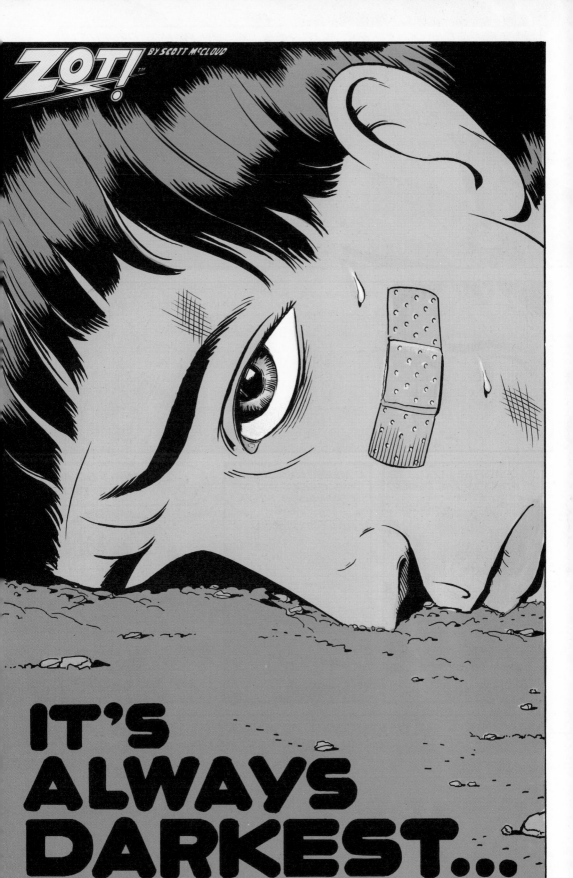

# ZOT!

BY SCOTT McCLOUD

# IT'S ALWAYS DARKEST...

bob lappan
LETTERER

DENIS McFARLING
COLORIST

KURT BUSIEK &
ADAM PHILIPS
CONSULTANTS

DEAN MULLANEY &
CAT YRONWODE
EDITORS

THE PLANET IS CALLED *SIRIUS IV*. HE'S CALLED *PRINCE DRUFUS...* AS FOR THE REST:

WHAT *HAPPENED..?* THAT *THIEF*, VIC...JUMPED IN MY SHIP...MADE ME *CRASH...* BUT WHY AM I *ALIVE..?*

GUESS I *EJECTED* IN TIME...THROWN CLEAR...

≋ UNNH ≋

HURTS, JUST *GETTING UP...* AND SO *HOT* HERE...

BUT, WHAT ABOUT *VIC* ??

FOOTPRINTS.

THE SHIP VIC STOLE *CRASHED* OVER THAT WAY...

OH, OF ALL THE PEOPLE TO BE *STUCK IN THE DESERT* WITH--!

HEY *DRUFUS!!*

*C'MERE!* LOOK AT ALL THIS *GREAT STUFF* I SALVAGED FROM THE CRASH!

GO AWAY!

OH, COME ON!

I *MEAN* IT! GO AWAY!! I DON'T WANT TO *TALK* TO YOU!!

JUST LEAVE ME ALO--O**OOOW**!!

MY ANKLE! MY ANKLE! ARRRR...

IT'S *BROKEN!* I *KNOW* IT IS!

HOLD ON! DON'T TRY TO MOVE!

SOON... OKAY, SO *WHAT ELSE* DID YOU FIND BESIDES A *FIRST-AID KIT* AND THESE *STUPID CLOTHES?*

HEY, DON'T KNOCK THE CLOTHES.

SNIP!

WHEN THAT *SUN* COMES UP AGAIN, YOU'LL BE GLAD YOU HAVE SOMETHING *LOOSE* TO WEAR!

BESIDES, THE *LIGHT COLORS* WILL HELP *REFLECT THE HEAT.*

OH, *WHAT'S THE USE?!* WE'RE JUST GOING TO *STARVE,* ANYWAY!

NOT IF WE CAN FIND *CIVILIZATION* FIRST! TRY AN' *THINK POSITIVE!*

*"THINK POSITIVE",* HE SAYS... *HA!* EVEN IF I GET BACK TO THE PALACE, I *STILL* HAVEN'T FOUND THE KEY TO--

*HEY!*

THE KEY TO THE DOORWAY AT THE EDGE OF THE UNIVERSE! *YOU* HAD IT LAST! *WHERE IS IT?!*

OVER THERE.

IT WAS IN THE SHIP WHEN IT CRASHED. WE'RE GOING TO HAVE TO WAIT UNTIL THE FLAMES DIE DOWN SO WE CAN SEARCH THE WRECKAGE.

OH, *GREAT...*

WITH *MY* LUCK, IT'S ALREADY *MELTED!* OH, I CAN HEAR MY FATHER *NOW: "YOU'VE FAILED AGAIN, BOY! YOU'RE A DISGRACE TO THE ROYAL FAMILY!"*

HE'LL BE *RIGHT,* TOO...

*CUT IT OUT!*

3

THE ROYAL PALACE...

WHAT?!

IT'S *TRUE*, ZOT!

THE KING IS *DEAD!* *MURDERED!!* THEY DID IT JUST *LAST NIGHT!*

*GEEZ--!* AND I TALKED TO HIM RIGHT *BEFORE* THAT!!

WHO WOULD'VE THOUGHT THEY'D GO *THIS* FAR?!!

IT'S ALL PART OF A *DREADFUL CONSPIRACY!* MY EMPLOYER--MR. TWIK--IS *ONE OF THEM!* HE ACTUALLY KEPT *RECORDS* OF THEIR *MEETINGS.* THAT'S HOW I *ACCIDENTALLY DISCOVERED* THEIR PLANS...OH, BUT I DON'T KNOW WHAT TO DO! I SUCH A *COWARD*, MR., Uh...

CALL ME MAX. AND YOU'RE VERY *BRAVE*, MR. WHITHERS! BUT, WHY DID YOU COME TO *US* AND NOT THE *AUTHORITIES?*

OH, BUT WHO COULD I *TRUST?* ANYONE AT ALL MIGHT BE *INVOLVED!*

OF PRINCE *DRUFUS!* AND ZOT IS SO *GOOD* AND *PURE* AND *BRAVE* AND --

WELL, LET'S NOT GET *CARRIED AWAY...*

MR. WHITHERS, MY NAME IS *TAYLOR.* MY SON *VICTOR* DISCOVERED THIS CONSPIRACY SOME TIME AGO. I'M SURE WE CAN FIND A WAY TO *STOP* THEM!

AND AS LONG AS *OUR* INVOLVEMENT REMAINS SECRET, *YOURS* SHOULD AS WELL.

BUT IT'S NOT *ME* YOU SHOULD WORRY ABOUT, MR. TAYLOR...

IT'S THE *QUEEN!*

THOSE MEN REALIZE THAT EVEN THOUGH *DRUFUS* IS NOW THE *CROWN PRINCE*, THE QUEEN WILL STILL HAVE THE MOST *INFLUENCE* ON HIM!

THEY SAY SHE'S *SMART* ENOUGH TO *GUESS* WHAT'S HAPPENED--

4

"--SO THEY'VE DECIDED TO KILL HER, TOO, THIS EVENING!"

MY QUEEN, HOW NICE TO *SEE* YOU AGAIN! DID YOU ENJOY YOUR TRIP TO THE *COLONIES*?

NO, I DID *NOT*, MR. SWIMBLER. AND YOU NEEDN'T PRETEND YOU'RE GLAD TO SEE ME.

ALL IS IN *READINESS*, YOUR GRACE.

IF YOU'LL JUST *STEP THIS WAY*...THE KING WILL BE WITH YOU SHORTLY...

KINDLY REMOVE THAT HAND, SIR...

THIS WAY, *YOUR GRACE*...

BE *SEEING* YOU.

MY *ASSISTANT* IS JUST *TIDYING UP* A BIT, YOUR GRACE...

HE'LL BE *DONE* SOON.

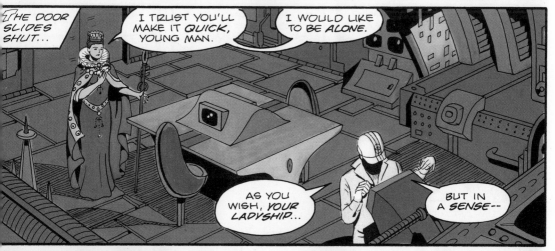

THE DOOR SLIDES SHUT...

I TRUST YOU'LL MAKE IT *QUICK*, YOUNG MAN.

I WOULD LIKE TO BE *ALONE*.

AS YOU WISH, *YOUR LADYSHIP*...

BUT IN A *SENSE*--

--YOU ALREADY *ARE*.

WH--WHAT IS THE *MEANING* OF THIS?! WHO ARE YOU??

I'M CALLED J-9-A-C-9-K, YOUR LADYSHIP...KNOWN VARIOUSLY AS 9-JACK-9, MR. 9, OR SIMPLY "JACK".

YOU CAN CALL ME *DEATH*.

5

WHAT DO YOU M--?

BOOM!

EH?

OH, IT'S *YOU!* WOULD YOU *HOLD ON* A MOMENT? I'VE GOT AN *ASSASSINATION* TO DO.

FORGET IT, "JACK"!!

THE KING WAS YOUR *LAST VICTIM.* I'M HERE TO MAKE *SURE* OF THAT!

YOUNG MAN, ARE YOU SAYING THAT-- THAT--

--THAT I *OFFED* YOUR *HUSBAND,* MADAM?

YES, I'M AFRAID THAT'S *EXACTLY* WHAT HE'S SAYING!

AND HE *APPARENTLY* THINKS HE CAN STOP ME FROM DOING *YOU* IN, AS WELL...

NO, JACK...I *KNOW* I CAN STOP YOU!!

REALLY?

WELL, IN *THAT* CASE, I *SUPPOSE* I SHOULD JUST--

"TOSS MY HAT IN THE RING," EH?

UH... WELL, I...

HUNH?

GONE!

YOUNG MAN, IS IT *TRUE*?? HAS THE KING BEEN *MURDERED*?! IF THIS IS SOME KIND OF *JOKE*--!

HEY!! LOOK OUT!!

GUESS WHO?

*AAAH!!*

BLAM!

LEAVE HER ALONE!

ONLY STUNNED...*JEEZ*!.. HOW DID HE *DO* THAT?! AND WHERE DID HE--?

OH, *THERE* YOU ARE...

FANCY TRICK, JACK.

OH, IT'S NOTHING.

HOPE YOU DON'T MIND I SLIPPED INTO SOMETHING MORE *COMFORTABLE*...

NOW, AS FOR OUR *ROYAL WIDOW* HERE, WHAT SAY WE STRIKE A *DEAL*?

SHE DIES. YOU LIVE.

SORRY, JACK! OLE' *ZACH PALEOZOGT* DOESN'T MAKE DEALS!

DID YOU SAY "*PALEOZOGT*"?

HMM...

YOU KNOW, I *KILLED* A COUPLE BY THAT NAME...

ANY RELATION?

7

THE SUN WILL BE *UP* SOON... OH, AS IF IT WASN'T HOT ENOUGH *NOW!*

⸮Sigh⸮ I WAS *HOPING* WE MIGHT FIND *SOMETHING* THAT COULD *SHADE US BEFORE* THIS...

HEY, MAYBE WE CAN *DIG OURSELVES* SOME SHADE

OH, *RATS!* NO USE...

...SAND WON'T *PACK*...

IT'S GONNA BE A *LONG DAY*...

~TEE-HEE-HEE~ WE *GOT* HER, BOYS! SHE'S AS GOOD AS *DEAD!*

~AHEM~

SWIMBLER YOU *CRETIN* HOW *DARE* YOU RETURN HERE

WHA--WHATEVER DO YOU *MEAN,* GENERAL SHRAPP??

FANCY *TRICK,* JACK.

OH, IT'S NOTHING.

*THERE!* IS THAT *HINT* ENOUGH FOR YOU?!

...

~TSK~ ~TS I *TOLD* Y THIS PLA WOULD G *MESSY*

*BLAST IT,* TWIK! IF WE WERE ALL AS *PICKY* AS *YOU,* WE'D *NEVER* GET A THING DONE!!

DON'T YOU RAISE YOUR VOICE AT *ME,* SWIMBLER!

*SILENCE!!* THE *BOTH* OF YOU! ONE MORE *CHIRP* AND I'LL *CRUSH* BOTH YOUR *LITTLE HEADS!*

I'LL *SECOND* THAT, VON CLOKMANN.

NOW, AS FOR *YOU,* SWIMBLER, WHAT DO YOU SUGGEST WE DO *NOW?*

AND THIS BETTER BE *GOOD*

=EH-HEH= W-WELL, FIRSTLY, GENERAL, I SUGGEST WE DO SOMETHING ABOUT THIS "ZOT" BOY'S FRIENDS--

OBVIOUSLY, SWIMBLER! I'VE ALREADY GIVEN THE ORDER.

=EH-HEH= YES, OF COURSE... NOW--AS SOON AS JACK FINISHES OFF THE QUEEN AND ZOT, WE CAN ROUND UP ANY OTHERS WHO KNOW OF OUR PLANS...

THEN, WHEN PRINCE DRUFUS IS FOUND--

HOW DO YOU KNOW HE WILL BE FOUND?

"HOW"? =EH-HEH=, WELL, OF COURSE HE WILL! OTHERWISE WE DON'T HAVE OUR ROYAL HEIR! SOMEONE ELSE WOULD CLAIM THE THRONE!

=HEH-HEH!= COULDN'T HAVE THAT! I'D BE OUT OF A JOB!

NEW ROYAL FAMILY. NEW ROYAL ADVISOR.

=TSK-TSK= PO-O-OR WEEVIS SWIMBLER...HOW WILL HE EVER PAY HIS SHARE OF MR. 9'S FEE WITH NO ACCESS TO THE ROYAL COFFERS?

AND HOW COULD HE POSSIBLY BE OF USE TO US IF HE NO LONGER HOLDS HIS POSITION OF POWER, HM?

RELAX, SWIMBLER...DRUFUS MAY YET RETURN.

IN THE MEANTIME, WHY DON'T YOU JUST--

SIT DOWN AND SHUT UP.

11

VIC, MY **ARMS** ARE GETTING TIRED!

THEN LET DOWN THE **KNAPSACK.**

BUT I'LL **COOK!**

THEN **DON'T LET** DOWN! WHAT DO YOU **WANT** FROM ME?!

VIC, DIDN'T YOU SAY OUR THERMOS HAS ONLY ABOUT A **QUART OF WATER** IN IT? I MEAN...THAT'LL HARDLY EVEN LAST A **DAY!** WHAT'LL WE **DO?!**

WE'LL MAKE IT LAST **LONGER!** WE WENT THROUGH THIS **ALREADY,** STUPID! WE'LL DO WHAT WE **HAVE** TO DO! THAT'S ALL THERE IS TO IT!

OH, I'M GONNA **DIE,** I JUST **KNOW** IT...

**SHUT UP.**

I MEAN IT! WE'RE BOTH GONNA **DIE** IN THIS CRUMMY DESERT!!

IT'S **USELESS** TO TRY AND **FIGHT** IT!

WHY SHOULD I **WANT** TO LIVE ANY **LONGER,** ANYWAY? I'VE BEEN A **MISERABLE FAILURE** ALL MY LIFE...

NOBODY WOULD EVEN **CARE** IF I WAS GONE...

FATHER WOULD SAY IT WAS **MY OWN FAULT**... MOTHER HARDLY EVEN KNOWS I **EXISTED**...

I MIGHT AS WELL **BURN UP** RIGHT NOW AND--!

**STOP IT!!**

**STOP WHINING!!**

I...I'M SORRY, VIC... I KNOW IT'S HARD ENOUGH F-FOR YOU, WITHOUT M-ME **COMPLAINING** ALL THE TIME...

HEY, I'M SORRY I **YELLED** AT YOU, DRU... ARE YOU GONNA BE **OKAY?** I MEAN, YOU SOUND AWFULLY **SHAKY**...MAYBE YOU OUGHTTA PUT UP YOUR **KNAPSACK** AGAIN...

IN A MINUTE...

12

IT'S JUST THAT...WELL, I'M SCARED TOO, BUT AS LONG AS THERE'S SOME CHANCE...UH... LET'S NOT GIVE UP SO SOON, O.K.?

DRU..?

...

VIC, WHAT IS THIS THING I'VE BEEN USING AS A WALKING STICK?

THAT? I DUNNO... I GOT IT OUT OF THE SHIP.

IT WAS WITH A LOT OF BEACH STUFF. Y'KNOW, TOWELS, BATHING SUITS...

IT'S GOT SOME WRITING ON IT...

ANGLE AWAY FROM USER BEFORE PRESSING RELEASE SWITCH

HUH! SO, WHERE'S THIS "RELEASE SWITCH"?

I DON'T KN-- OH, HERE IT IS.

CLK!

FLUMP!

I JUST KNEW WE SHOULD'VE BROUGHT THOSE FOLDING CHAIRS...

13

MAX, ARE YOU SURE WE SHOULD'VE LET ZOT TAKE ON 9-JACK-9 *ALONE?* I MEAN, COULDN'T WE AT LEAST SEND PEABODY TO *HELP* HIM?

I DON'T MEAN TO *ALARM* YOU, JENNY, BUT AT THIS POINT IT COULDN'T HURT TO HAVE SOME PROTECTION OF *OUR OWN*...

BUT, IS THIS *"PEABODY"* ROBOT OF YOURS PROTECTION *ENOUGH?*

YOU *KIDDIN'*, BALDY?!

*PEEBZ* HERE CAN ZAP A BUG AT *30 PACES!* I MEAN, *HELL*, HE'S BETTER'N *BLACK FLAG!*

*YOU* TELL 'IM, DOC!

YES, WELL, BUTCH *IS* RIGHT ABOUT PEABODY'S ABILITY... OF COURSE, HE WAS ORIGINALLY DESIGNED AS A BUTLER ONLY...

ZACH AND I DID..."*SOUP HIM UP*" A BIT, SINCE--

*FREEZE!!* ALL OF YOU! YOU'RE UNDER ARREST!

*US??* ON WHAT *CHARGE*, CAPTAIN?!

≠AK!!≠

OH, I *KNEW* IT! WE'RE *DONE FOR!!*

SIR! THE ROBOT HAS A *GUN!*

ELIMINATE HIM, SOLDIER!!

NO, STOP! HE WON'T *HARM* YOU! IT'S NOT IN HIS PR--!

BLAM!

≠KGK≠

≠KLIK! KRAAK!≠ ≠BZZT! BZZT.!≠

YOU *RATS!* CUT IT *OUT!!*

BLAM!

BRAK!

*CUT IT OUT!!*

SKKY!

AARG!

WE *TOLD* YA HE WASN'T GONNA *ZAP* ANYBODY! *CUT IT OUT!!*

*WHY, YOU--!*

*ANNIHILATE THAT MONKEY!!*

≥AK!≤ ≥AK!≤

BLAM! BLAM!

HE WENT OUT THE *WINDOW!* NOW WE'LL GET HIM!

AW, CRAP! DUMB LEDGE IS *SLIPPERY!*

*YOW!*

BLAM!

≥UNGF!≤ *NYAAH! NYAAH!*

THOUGHT YA *HAD* ME, HUH?

CHAK!

WOOO! WOOo! WOOo! WOOO!

SIR, THE CHIMP HAS *ESCAPED.*

I'VE GOT TO *GET AWAY* SOMEHOW! FIND BUTCH... WARN ZOT...BUT *HOW??*

IF *ZOT* WERE HERE, HE'D JUST GRAB *PEABODY'S GUN* OFF THAT *CHAIR* AND... AND...

NEVER MIND! WE'LL GET HIM *LATER!*

AND...

OBOY...

15

BUT, FATHER, I TRIED... REALLY I TRIED.

DON'T PUNISH ME, PLEASE! I... I KNOW I'M NOT WORTHY, FATHER...

BUT I NEVER WANTED TO BE KING LIKE YOU...

I N--I-- ≤HUNH?≥

DRUFUS! WAKE UP! C'MON! IT'S TIME FOR LUNCH!

LUNCH? OH, YEAH. FOOD!

SO WHAT'S ON THE MENU, HUNH?

OUR SPECIAL OF THE DAY: 4 SIPS OF WATER AND 2½ CUBES OF LAUGHING COW® CHEESE...

AAH, A MEAL FIT FOR A KING!

AFTER LUNCH...

...SO THERE WE WERE IN THE FANCIEST RESTAURANT ON THE PLANET AND UNCLE ZARBIM WOULDN'T EVEN LET ME HAVE SECONDS!

NOW WAIT A MINUTE!

THIS GUY ZARBIM MAY BE A GENERAL, BUT YOU'RE A PRINCE! HE CAN'T PUSH YOU AROUND LIKE THAT. YOU SHOULD PULL RANK ON HIM!

YOU DON'T KNOW UNCLE ZARBIM. HE'S REALLY STRICT.

HEY, YOU SHOULD MEET MY FATHER. SHEESH, TALK ABOUT "STRICT"!

BUT AT LEAST I'VE LEARNED TO STAND UP TO HIM WHEN I HAVE TO.

YEAH, WELL, THAT'S YOU.

HEY, I'LL TEACH YOU HOW! C'MON! I'LL BE ZARBIM AND YOU BE YOU, O.K.?

UH... O.K.!

SO, WHAT DO YOU WANT, BOY?!

≤Ahem!≥ UNCLE, I DEMAND THAT YOU LET ME HAVE SOME ICE CREAM!

YOU WHAT?!

AAH!! DON'T HIT ME!

16

=Sigh...=

Uh...I MEAN *YOU* CAN'T TALK TO *ME* THAT WAY!

AND *WHY NOT*, BOY?!

BECAUSE I'M A *PRINCE*, YOU OLD *WINDBAG!!* AND YOU BETTER START *TREATING* ME LIKE ONE!!

WHY *YOU--!*

*SHUT UP, UNCLE!* YOU'VE BEEN P--PUSHING ME AROUND LONG ENOUGH!

THIS MAY COME AS A *SHOCK* TO YOU, UNCLE, BUT I'VE GOT A *MIND OF MY OWN!* YEAH, THAT'S RIGHT!

AND MAYBE *I* KNOW WHAT'S BEST FOR ME AS MUCH AS *YOU* DO! AND-- AND MAYBE *MORE* THAN YOU DO!!

I'LL TELL YOUR *FATHER* ABOUT THIS, *BOY!*

OH *NO*, YOU WON'T! *I'LL* TELL HIM!

AND *THIS* TIME I'LL MAKE SURE HE *LISTENS!*

HMM...MAYBE HE *WILL*, BOY. MAYBE HE *WILL*...

BUT YOU *STILL* CAN'T HAVE ANY *ICE-CREAM!*

*AT* LONG LAST, NIGHT FALLS AGAIN...

AH, COOL AND DARK! DARK AND COOL! I LOVE IT!

MM! ME, TOO!

BUT YOU KNOW WHAT THEY SAY:"*IT'S ALWAYS DARKEST BEFORE THE DAWN.*"

=HMF!= THANKS...

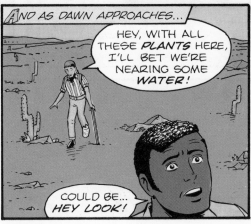

*A*ND AS DAWN APPROACHES...

HEY, WITH ALL THESE *PLANTS* HERE, I'LL BET WE'RE NEARING SOME *WATER!*

COULD BE... HEY LOOK!

I'M NOT SURE, BUT--

YES! IT IS! A *RESCUE SHIP!!*

17

WHAT--

--DID YOU--

--SAY??

I *THOUGHT* I SPOKE CLEARLY ENOUGH. I SAID I *KILLED* A COUPLE NAMED PALEOZOGT...

*TALL RUGGED FELLOW* AND HIS WIFE.

ABOUT *THREE YEARS* BACK, I THINK...THE *KING* ORDERED IT...

YOU'RE LYING...

*YOU'RE LYING!!*

NOW WHY ON EARTH WOULD I LIE ABOUT SOMETHING LIKE *THAT?*

YOU'RE A *SPY!* YOU *CHECKED UP* ON ME! YOU KNOW *MY PARENTS* LEFT ME THREE YEARS AGO! YOU'RE JUST TRYING TO MAKE ME *MAD!!*

KRASH

THEY WERE YOUR *PARENTS?* OH, I'M SORRY, I DIDN'T KNOW...

OWW..!

YOU MUST ADMIT, THOUGH... I *AM* MAKING YOU MAD..

HE'S RIGHT!

I'VE GOT TO STAY *CALM!* IN CONTROL! I KNOW HE'S JUST TRYING TO *TRICK* ME!

I *KNOW* IT!

18

COME ON OUT, JACK! I'M *READY* FOR YOU NOW!

IT'S NOT SOME *HELPLESS VICTIM* THIS TIME! NOW YOU'RE UP AGAINST A *REAL CHALLENGE!*

AGREED!

IN FACT, YOU'VE BEEN *SUCH A "CHALLENGE"*--

≶GKK!≷

--YOU'VE EVEN EARNED MY *PERSONAL TOUCH.*

BOOM!!

WHAT? *ANOTHER* ONE?? OH, *TAKE A NUMBER,* WILL YOU? I'M *BUSY!*

THE SHOTS STRIKE JACK *DEAD CENTER,* AGAIN AND AGAIN--

OH, THAT'S QUITE *FUTILE,* MISS...

TRUTH TO TELL, ONLY MY *HANDS* HAVE ANY SORT OF *MASS* JUST NOW...

OUT OF SHOTS!

WHAT DO I DO *NOW?*

19

MR. WHITHERS TOLD US THAT JACK SORT OF "POSSESSES" ELECTRONIC CIRCUITRY...

MAYBE I DON'T KNOW MUCH ABOUT HOW HE WORKS--

BUT I REMEMBER THAT WHEN BUTCH WAS FOOLING AROUND WITH ELECTRONICS--

--MOM ALWAYS SAID BE CAREFUL OF ONE THING...

KKREEE!!!

POP
POP
POP
SPLASH!

≥COUGH!≥
≥COUGH!≥
GASP!≥

≥KKHREEE

≥K-K!≥

≥KRRK!≥≥T-T-
≥T-T-T≥

≥T-T-ZT-T--≥

TOUCHE

BLINK!

SOON... THEN IT IS *TOO LATE* TO SAVE MY HUSBAND...I SEE.

I'M SURE HE WAS A *GREAT MAN*...

NO, BOY...THE KING WAS A *SELFISH, CORRUPT* AND *EGOTISTICAL TYRANT.*

BUT HE *WAS* MY *HUSBAND,* HE *WAS* KING, AND HE *WILL* BE AVENGED!

THIS IS THE CORRIDOR THEY WERE LEADING US DOWN WHEN I *BROKE FREE.*

WITH OR *WITHOUT* PEABODY'S GUN, THAT WAS A PRETTY *BRAVE THING* TO DO, JEN!

ONLY *NEXT* TIME, I HOPE *I'LL* GET TO DO SOME *LIFE-SAVING!*

I'VE GOT A *REP* TO PROTECT, Y'KNOW...

ZOT! LOOK OUT!

??

HALT!! DROP YOUR WEAPONS!

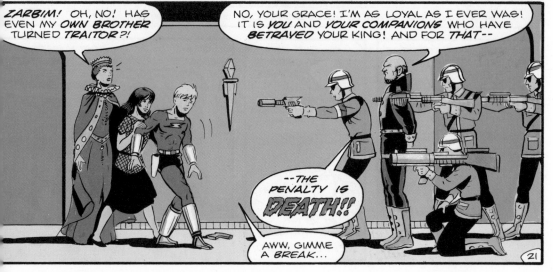

*ZARBIM!* OH, NO! HAS EVEN MY *OWN BROTHER* TURNED *TRAITOR?!*

NO, YOUR GRACE! I'M AS LOYAL AS I EVER WAS! IT IS *YOU* AND *YOUR COMPANIONS* WHO HAVE *BETRAYED* YOUR KING! AND FOR *THAT*--

--THE PENALTY IS *DEATH!!*

AWW, GIMME A BREAK...

21

--THAT THE ONE WHO STOLE *THE KEY*--

--IS TO BE *SHOT ON SIGHT!*

HE'S TOO *SCARED* TO MOVE!

I'VE GOT TO DO *SOMETHING!*

AAR!

NO!!

LOOK OUT!

CLIK!

AAAHH!

BLAM!

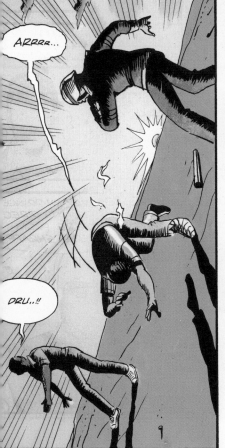

ARRRR...

DRU..!!

I KILLED HIM!!

I KILLED THE *PRINCE...!*

NO..!!

G·GET US OUT OF HERE, LIEUTENANT!

NOW!!

NO! *STOP!!* HE'S STILL ALIVE!

COME BACK!!

HE'S

CLIK

VRUU-UUUUM!

23

OW!

≈ Sigh...≈

WELL, THAT'S *ONE WOUND* HEALED, AT LEAST...WE CAN GET THE OTHER *NINETY-NINE* LATER...

HURT MUCH?

*DREEP!*

NO...KINDA *NUMB*, REALLY...

Y'KNOW, I'VE BEEN *KNOCKED AROUND* SO MUCH SINCE I WAS A KID...IT ALWAYS MADE ME FEEL LIKE A *JERK* BEFORE...THIS TIME'S *DIFFERENT*, SOMEHOW...

YEAH, NOW IT'S *MY* TURN TO FEEL LIKE A JERK.

I MEAN, HERE *I'M* THE ONE WHO *STARTED* IT ALL ON ACCOUNT OF SOME *STUPID PRANK!*

I DON'T BLAME *YOU*, VIC... I KNOW YOU ONLY KEPT THE *KEY* 'CAUSE IT SEEMED LIKE THE RIGHT THING TO DO... I JUST...

I JUST HAD TO BLAME *SOMEONE.*

WAKE ME AFTER *SUNDOWN*, O.K.?

YEAH, YEAH...

DRU, WHAT I'M TRYING TO SAY IS...WELL, I WAS AFRAID I'D NEVER GET A CHANCE TO THANK YOU...

NO NEED, VIC... FORGET IT...

2

YAWN!

RISE AND SHINE!

C'MON. *GET UP, LAZYBONES!* I'VE GOT A *SURPRISE* FOR YOU.

Y'KNOW THAT OL' *KEY* OF OURS? THE ONE I SAID WAS IN THE *WRECKAGE?*

WELL, UH... ≈*HEH-HEH*≈

I GUESS I DID, UMM... *STRETCH THE TRUTH* A BIT IN THE INTERESTS OF *GALACTIC SECURITY...*

...MEANING THAT I DIDN'T *TRUST* YOU YET...

...UT NOW THAT I ...NOW YOU A LOT *BETTER--*

--AND I CAN TELL THAT...

THAT YOU...

25

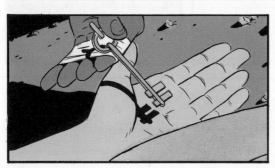

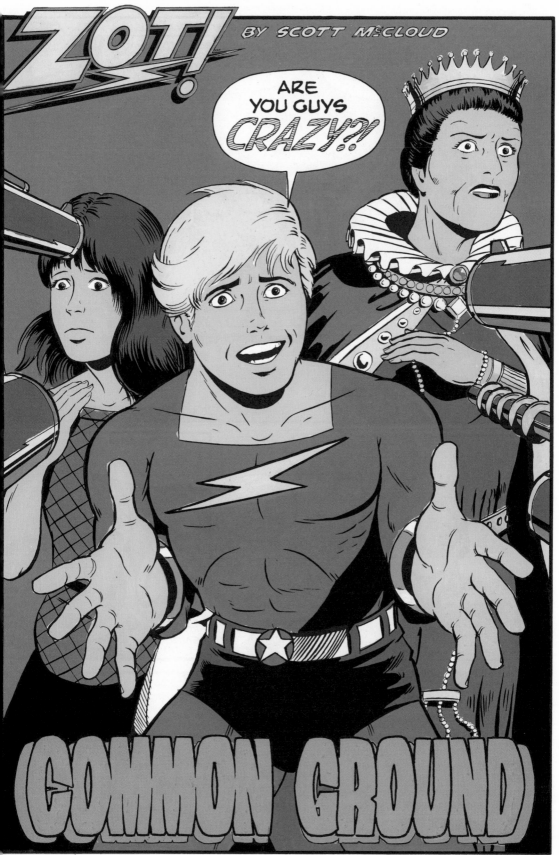

bob lappan LETTERER / DENIS McFARLING COLORIST / KURT BUSIEK & ADAM PHILIPS CONSULTANTS / CAT @ YRONWODE & DEAN MULLANEY EDITORS

VERY WELL, MY SISTER... YOU MAY HAVE *FIVE MINUTES...*

*FIVE MINUTES LATER...*

JENNY, I'M SORRY YOU HAD TO GET *MIXED UP* IN THIS...

I *DON'T LIKE* THIS, SIR! MAYBE WE SHOULD CHECK INSIDE.

THE GENERAL CAN TAKE CARE OF *HIMSELF,* DERWOOD!

IT'S NOT *YOUR* FAULT, ZOT. I'M JUST WORRIED ABOUT *POOR BUTCH*...HE COULD BE *ANYWHERE* ON THIS CRAZY PLANET.

DON'T WORRY, JEN. WE'LL FIND YOUR BROTHER! EVERYTHING'LL BE BACK TOGETHER IN *NO TIME,* YOU'LL SEE!

~ sigh ~

YOU REALLY *DO* COME FROM A *WHOLE DIFFERENT WORLD,* DON'T YOU? I'LL BET YOU WOULDN'T BE SO *CONFIDENT* ALL THE TIME IF YOU GREW UP ON *MY* EARTH...

THINK MAYBE I SHOULDN'T *BRAG* SO MUCH, JEN?

NAAH... WHO NEEDS *ANOTHER* HUMBLE GOOD GUY? MAYBE YOU *ARE* A JERK SOMETIMES, ZOT... BUT YOU'RE THE NICEST JERK *I* EVER MET... I DON'T WANT YOU TO CHANGE A *THING...*

♡AWWW.

DON'T LET THAT *"SWEET"* ACT *FOOL* YA, HARRY! THEY'RE *DANGEROUS ASSASSINS!*

CLIK!

THEY'RE COMING *BACK OUT,* MEN!

EHH... DROP YOUR WEAPONS...

③

NO WAY, ZOT! BUTCH IS *MY BROTHER!* I'M NOT GONNA SIT AROUND AND *WAIT* FOR NEWS!

IT'S *TOO DANGEROUS*, JENNY! YOU'VE GOTTA LET ME HANDLE THIS *ALONE!*

DON'T YOU *TRUST* ME TO DO THE JOB RIGHT?

HEY, *YOU KNOW* THAT'S NOT WHAT I MEANT! BUT-- BUT--

JEEZ, ZOT! HE'S NOT *YOUR* BROTHER! YOU DON'T EVEN *LIKE* HIM!

AWW, HE'S ALL RIGHT... THAT'S NOT THE POINT, JENNY!

I JUST THINK YOU'LL BE *SAFER* AT...

...UH, WHERE DID YOU SAY WE WERE GOING, *YOUR MAJESTY?*

THE *SACRED CATHEDRAL* ON THE ISLAND OF *SHOTARO!* THE FAITHFUL THERE ARE *SURE* TO GIVE US SANCTUARY!

NOT EVEN *THE TRAITORS* WHO PURSUE US WOULD DARE TO ATTACK *THERE!* TO DO SO WOULD BE *SACRILEGE!*

*GREAT!* NOW IF WE JUST KNEW WHERE *MAX* AND THE OTHERS WERE TAKEN...

I'D WAGER THAT THEY'VE BEEN SENT TO THE *PRISON TOWERS* AT THE CITY'S *NORTH SECTOR*, BOY!

6

THE PURSUERS ARE AT LAST EVADED, DIRECTIONS ARE GIVEN AND--

I BETTER GO NOW, JENNY...

ZOT, I'VE *GOT* TO COME WITH YOU. *PLEASE!* I DON'T CARE HOW *DANGEROUS* IT IS!

ALL I KNOW IS THAT I'M NOT GONNA RISK LOSING YOU *AND* BUTCH THE SAME DAY...

NOT ON *THIS* WORLD... *PLEASE...*

WELL, I...

YEAH, O.K...

C'MON...

*FAREWELL,* THEN, YOUNG ONES! MAY THE *SPIRIT OF THE KEY* GRANT YOU SPEED!

SAME TO *YOU,* YOUR HIGHNESS!

YEAH, *GOOD LUCK!*

ISN'T HE JUST THE *MOST DELIGHTFUL* YOUNG MAN, ZARBIM?

GRRRR...

7

① ONCE OUTSIDE THE MAMMOTH WALLS OF SIRIUS IV'S WEALTHY CAPITAL...

WOW...I GUESS *NOT EVERYTHING* ON SIRIUS IS SO *RITZY*, HUH...?

I THINK PLACES LIKE THIS ARE THE *RULE*, JEN... NOT THE EXCEPTION...

NOW YOU KNOW WHERE THEY FOUND ALL THOSE *"COMMON FOLK"* FOR OUR CEREMONIES...

8

"GEEZ, I... I DIDN'T KNOW IT WAS *THIS* BAD..."

..THIS IS ONLY THE SECOND TIME I'VE BEEN AWAY FROM *MY EARTH*...

UH-HUH.

HEY, *WAIT A MINUTE.* WHAT DO YOU MEAN "ONLY THE *SECOND TIME*"?

I'D READ SOMEWHERE THAT YOU'D BEEN "*ON A DOZEN WORLDS*" AND--AND "*SAVED THE LIVES OF THOUSANDS*"!

OH, *THAT?!* YOU FELL FOR THAT ??!

⸫HA!! HA!⸫

NAW, THAT'S JUST *HYPE* BY SOME *P.R. MAN* WE HIRED! WE HAD TO GET RID OF HIM WHEN HE STARTED PRINTING THINGS THAT *WEREN'T TRUE*...

OH...

UH...I *HAVE* BEEN ON A *COUPLE OF* WORLDS...

...SAVED THE LIVES OF *DOZENS*...

⸫ sigh...⸫ IT'LL *DO*, ZOT...

IT'LL DO...

9

IN THE PRISON TOWERS --

--THE CONSPIRATORS MEET...

I ARRIVED AS SOON AS *POSSIBLE*, GENERAL SHRAPP!

AS *ALWAYS*, YOU'RE *RIGHT ON TIME*, MR. TWIK! I WAS JUST TELLING THESE *FLEAS* WHAT'S *IN STORE* FOR THEM IF THEY *DON'T TALK!*

WELL, I TRUST WE'LL BE *DONE* WITH THEM *SOON*. I HAVE A *MEETING* TO ATTEND TO!

OH, IT WON'T TAKE LONG...

NOW, FOR THE *LAST TIME*, OLD MAN, *WHO ARE YOU WORKING FOR?*

AND AS I TOLD YOU *ALREADY*, SIR, I'M *SELF-EMPLOYED* AND *PROUD OF IT!*

AND WHO'RE *YOU* CALLING "OLD"??

BAH! TORTURE WOULD BE *QUICKER!*

YES! YES! *VON CLOKMANN* IS RIGHT! *TORTURE* THEM!

QUIET, SWIMBLER!

NOW AS FOR *YOU*, SIR; WHAT PART DO *YOU* PLAY IN ALL THIS?

WHATEVER PART I *CAN* PLAY IN STOPPING YOU WORMS! JUST AS MY SON *VICTOR* DID *BEFORE* ME!

HMPH! AND WHAT OF YOUR *COWARDLY FRIEND*, H--? ⸕GASP⸖

*WHITHERS??*

MR. TWIK, I'M *SORRY!*

10

B-BUT YOU KEPT SUCH *COMPLETE RECORDS* OF THESE *MEETINGS*...I ONLY DISCOVERED THEM BY *ACCIDENT*...I DIDN'T MEAN ANY *HARM*, BUT--

--BUT, WELL, I COULDN'T LET YOU KILL THE *QUEEN!* I HAD TO DO *SOMETHING!*

SO *YOU* WERE THE LEAK, TWIK!!

N-N-NOW, *G-GENTLEMEN!* ONE *MUST* KEEP *RECORDS!* SURELY YOU WON'T HOLD AN *INNOCENT* MIS-MISTAKE AGAINST ME!

HEH... HEH...

*BUNGLER!!* YOU *KNEW* THE PENALTY FOR BETRAYING OUR *SECRETS!*

A PENALTY WE MAY *YET* FIND IT IN OUR HEARTS TO *SPARE* YOU, TWIK--

BUT NOW THAT WE KNOW WHAT *THIS ONE'S* ROLE WAS THERE'S NO SUCH NEED FOR *MERCY!*

→Gulp!←

HANDS UP!!

→AAR!←

BR—
A—!
NO!

DROP YOUR WEAPONS! ALL OF YOU!!

UH...I THINK THAT'S THE ONLY WEAPON THEY HAD...

OH...

BRRIIINNGG!!

THE ALARM!

THIS PLACE'LL BE *CRAWLING* WITH *GUARDS* IN A MOMENT, ZACH. WE BETTER *GET MOVING!*

NO SWEAT, MAX.

I'M SURE THE GENERAL WILL BE *HAPPY* TO LEND US THE KEYS TO THAT *FLYER* OF HIS WE SAW DOCKED OUTSIDE...

11

T! YOW! HEY! WHOA! WH--WH--?!! G--! WH--? YOW! HEY!

THAT'S MY NEPHEW!

BUT NOT ALL THE PURSUING CRAFT CAN BE STOPPED IN TIME--!

GET INSIDE, GUYS! I'LL HOLD 'EM OFF!

YOU MEAN "WE" WILL!

I'M NOT GONNA LET YOU TAKE ON THESE CREEPS ALONE!

I CAN HANDLE IT, JEN! GET INSIDE, PLEASE!

I'M NOT MAKING ANY SACRIFICES! I'LL COME IN TOO, BUT NOT TILL EVERYONE ELSE IS!

O--OKAY, ZOT. I'M LEAVING!

GOOD! AND I'LL B--!

AAH!

JENNY!

UNGH,... I'M O.K. I'M O.K.! JUST SINGED A BIT!

HURRY UP, ZACH!

STEP ON IT!

COME ON!

≈WHEW!≈

"SIR! THEY'VE ALL ENTERED THE CATHEDRAL! WHAT NOW?"

KNOCK THE BLASTED *GATE IN*, CAPTAIN! BLOW UP THE WHOLE *ISLAND* IF YOU HAVE TO!! I WANT THOSE--

NO!

≈AAK!!≈

SIR? ARE YOU THERE?!

RESCIND THAT ORDER, GENERAL! I WON'T HAVE ONE *BRICK* OF OUR HOLIEST SHRINE DESECRATED! *NOT BY ANYONE!*

≈GGK≈ ≈GASP!≈ YOU MEAN YOU REALLY *BELIEVE* THA--?! ERRR, OF COURSE!! OF COURSE!! SORRY...

THUS, WITH THE FALL OF NIGHT...

...STALEMATE.

14

HEY, WE *NEEDED* A REST ANYWAY, *RIGHT?*

÷sigh÷

WELL, YOU ARE ALL WELCOME TO REST *HERE*, LAD--AS LONG AS YOU WISH.

ESPECIALLY IF IT IS *AGAINST* THE WISHES OF *GRAND INQUISITOR VON CLOKMANN!*

THIS TALK OF CONSPIRACY COMES AS *LITTLE SURPRISE* TO THOSE OF US WHO'VE HAD *DEALINGS* WITH HIM!

WE'VE SEEN HIS *CORRUPT INFLUENCE* ON THE HIGH PRIEST AND LEARNED OF HOW HE'S BENT OUR TEACHINGS TO SUIT HIS OWN *HATEFUL PURPOSES.*

UNFORTUNATELY, WE ARE VERY *ISOLATED* HERE...EVEN THE DAY'S NEWS MUST BE BROUGHT ON *PAPER* OR BY *WORD OF MOUTH*...

TRADITION DEMANDS THAT NO *ELECTRONIC DEVICES* OF ANY KIND BE ALLOWED *INSIDE!*

JUST BETWEEN US...TRADITION CAN BE A REAL *PAIN* IN THE NECK, SOMETIMES...

--THIS *PARTICULAR* TRADITION MAY PROVE A *VITAL DEFENSE* FOR US...

BE THAT AS IT MAY, *FATHER KIMM*--

YOU SEE, THE *ASSASSIN* WHO MURDERED MY HUSBAND AND, QUITE NEARLY *MYSELF,*\* IS IN SOME WAY *DEPENDENT* ON *ELECTRONIC CIRCUITRY!*

\* *ISSUES #5 AND #6 --SCOTT.*

HEY, THAT'S *RIGHT!* 9-JACK-9 CAN'T ATTACK US HERE! THERE'S NOTHING FOR HIM TO ZAP INTO...

NOW *THAT'S* LUCK!

YEAH...GEEZ...JUST *THINKING* ABOUT THAT GUY STILL GIVES ME THE *CREEPS*...

Y'KNOW HE *CHECKED UP* ON ME, MAX... FOUND OUT ABOUT MY PARENTS...

HE WANTS ME TO THINK THAT-- THAT HE *KILLED* THEM...

HE *WHAT??*

GOOD LORD, ZACH! HOW DO YOU KNOW IT ISN'T *TRUE?!*

15

C'MON, MAX! IT JUST DOESN'T *ADD UP!* MOM AND DAD MIGHT'VE WORKED FOR THE GOVERNMENT, BUT THEY WOULDN'T GET MIXED UP IN ANY *SPY-STUFF...* THEY WERE JUST *PAPER-PUSHERS!*

JACK'S JUST A *SICKIE,* THAT'S ALL...ANYONE WHO NAMES HIMSELF AFTER A KID'S *LULLABY* HAS *GOTTA* BE A SICKIE...

*"LULLABY"?*

YEAH, MY MOM USED TO SING ME TO SLEEP WITH IT...

"NINE, JACK, NINE, ROPE MADE OF TWINE, CIRCLED HIS OLD MOTHER'S HEAD. TIE, ROPE, TIE NINE FEET UP HIGH HUNG HER UNTIL SHE --"

GEEZ, I'D FORGOTTEN HOW *GROSS* THAT WAS...

ZACH...I'VE NEVER HEARD THAT *LULLABY...*

HUH? *SURE* YOU HAVE!

YOU WROTE THAT WHOLE *BOOK* ON NURSERY RHYMES ONCE! YOU'VE *GOTTA* KNOW *THIS* ONE, MAX. IT WAS IN THE *FAMILY!*

I'VE NEVER HEARD IT...

WELL, YOU DON'T THINK SHE'D *MAKE UP* A THING LIKE *THAT,* DO YOU?

WHY *WOULD* SHE? *UNLESS...*

OH MY GOD...

*"...SHE KNEW."*

YOUNG MAN, IT'S BEEN *TWO DAYS* NOW...I WON'T HAVE YOU AVOIDING ME IN THIS MANNER! YOUR PARENTS' FATE WAS *THE KING'S* DECISION, NOT MINE!

I'VE TOLD YOU HOW MUCH I *DETESTED* MY HUSBAND'S WAYS! BUT I HAD NO *CONTROL* OVER HIM!

*NONE!* DO YOU *UNDERSTAND?!*

16

YOU *LISTEN TO ME*, YOUNG MAN! I WASN'T *BORN* TO ROYALTY! MY FAMILY BELONGED TO ONE OF THE *LOWEST CLASSES* ON SIRIUS! NO ONE EVER *DISCOVERED* THAT, BUT *I* KNEW IT. I *ALWAYS* KNEW IT!

I'M DOING WHAT I CAN. I HAVE NOTHING TO *APOLOGIZE* FOR!

AT LEAST I'VE HAD *SOME INFLUENCE* OVER THE KING... OVER OUR SON...

IN TIME, I MAY *YET* SUCCEED IN STOPPING THIS *MADNESS*...

BUT, *NO!!* YOU WANT YOUR JUSTICE *NOW!* NOT LATER! WELL, IT--!

YOUR GRACE, WE HAVE NEWS FROM *OUTSIDE*...

*BAD*, I ASSUME, FROM THE LOOK ON YOUR FACE.

YOUR... YOUR GRACE...

THE PRINCE IS *DEAD*...

I SEE...

WELL, BOY--

--IT SEEMS WE'RE *EVEN*...

"NOW, AS NEAR AS WE CAN TELL, MR. TAYLOR'S SON, VIC, WAS FOUND *HALF-STARVED* AND DYING OF *THIRST*, SITTING BY *PRINCE DRUFUS'* BODY...

"*THE KEY* WAS WITH THEM...

"VIC WAS BRANDED *THE MURDERER*, BUT THIS MIGHT BE JUST A *CONVENIENT LIE*. WE DON'T KNOW YET...

"*NEVERTHELESS*, HE IS NOW BEING HELD FOR *PUBLIC EXECUTION*... IN TWO DAYS' TIME...

"THE KEY IS NOW IN THE HANDS OF *GRAND INQUISITOR VON CLOKMANN*..."

17

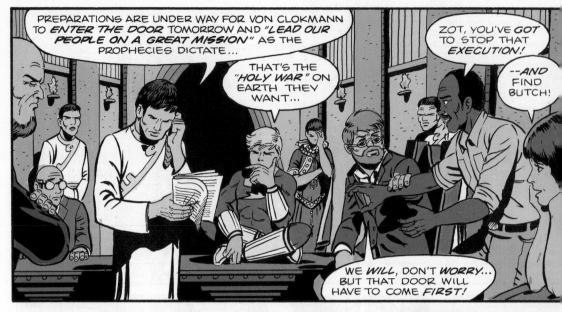

PREPARATIONS ARE UNDER WAY FOR VON CLOKMANN TO *ENTER THE DOOR* TOMORROW AND *"LEAD OUR PEOPLE ON A GREAT MISSION"* AS THE PROPHECIES DICTATE...

THAT'S THE "HOLY WAR" ON EARTH THEY WANT...

ZOT, YOU'VE *GOT* TO STOP THAT *EXECUTION!*

--AND FIND BUTCH!

WE *WILL*, DON'T *WORRY*... BUT THAT DOOR WILL HAVE TO COME *FIRST!*

IF MAX'S *ESCAPE ROUTE* WORKS, I'LL TAKE CARE OF *ALL THREE* OF THOSE JOBS, GUYS! THAT'S A *PROMISE!*

THEY'LL BE *MONITORING* THE WATERS, FATHER...CAN YOU PROVIDE A *DISTRACTION?*

HMM...

IF YOU CAN WAIT UNTIL DARK, I HAVE *JUST THE THING.*

*AT NIGHTFALL...*

*VOILA!* ACCORDING TO THOSE OLD *BLUEPRINTS* IN YOUR LIBRARY, THIS POOL SHOULD LEAD RIGHT OUT TO SEA!

WELL, *I'LL BE!* WE'RE FORTUNATE YOU HAVE SUCH A PENCHANT FOR BROWSING, MAX! I HAD NO IDEA THESE TUNNELS EVEN *EXISTED!*

WHY D'YA THINK THEY *BUILT* 'EM, MAX?

OH, MAYBE AS A *FEEDING ACCESS* FOR SOME *NOW-EXTINCT* ANIMAL...

OR PERHAPS IT WAS MEANT FOR THE SAME PURPOSE THAT IT WILL SERVE *TONIGHT*...

YEAH! *ESCAPE!*

SO... ANOTHER OPPORTUNITY FOR THE BRAT TO PLAY *HERO!* AND, AS USUAL WITH NO *HESITATION*...

IS *THAT* WHAT I PUSHED YOU SO HARD TO *BECOME*, DRUFUS?

WAS THAT ALL SO *IMPORTANT?*

18

○ OUTSIDE THE CATHEDRAL WALLS, THE *DEADLY TROOPS* MAINTAIN A *STERN VIGIL...*

AW, C'MON, BERT! LET *ME* TRY THE SCANNER, HUH? *PLEASE?!*

NOT NOW, ERNIE! I THINK I'VE *GOT* SOMETHING!

THOSE PRIESTS ARE DIPPING SOME LONG ROPES IN SOME KIND OF *LIQUID...* IT LOOKS LIKE THEY'RE *SPREADING* THEM ALL OVER THE OUTSIDE OF THE *CATHEDRAL.*

REALLY?

"YEAH, I THINK THIS IS THAT *'CEREMONY OF TORCHES'* I READ ABOUT ONCE...

"IN FACT, SOME GUY'S LEANING OUT THE WINDOW WITH A *TORCH* RIGHT NOW! THIS IS IT!"

WOW!!

WHOA!

CLAP CLAP

CLAP CLAP

:GASP!:

SAYY!

AWW, AIN'T THAT *PRETTY?*

HEY, YA THINK THEY'RE DOIN' IT JUST FOR *US,* BERT? HUH? DO YOU?

NAAH! THEY COULDN'T CARE *LESS* WHAT *WE* SEE OR DON'T--

HEY, DID YOU JUST *HEAR* SOMETHING?

NO, BERT...

19

THE NEXT MORNING, IN THE SPACE STATION CORRIDOR LEADING OUT TO THE "DOORWAY AT THE EDGE OF THE UNIVERSE..."

IT IS TIME...

MRMM...?

THE *NERVE* OF THOSE GUYS!

HEY, *I* WAS NEXT!

NO, ME! ME!!

ALL HAIL...

ALL HAIL...

SILENCE!

YES, FELLOW SIRIANS, OVER THE VAIN PROTESTS OF *HEATHEN OUTWORLDERS*, OUR BLESSED *GRAND INQUISITOR* HAS TAKEN CHARGE LIKE THE *GREAT LEADER* HE WAS *PROPHESIED* TO BE!

SOON, HE WILL ENTER THE HUGE AIR-FILLED *TRANSPARENT SPHERE* BUILT AROUND THE *SACRED DOOR*...

...THEN FLY TO THE DOOR ITSEL USING THE *CEREMONIAL JETPACK* AT THE SPHERE'S ENTRANCE!

SPHERE

DOOR — 1.5 KM

GREAT MAN

"EXTENSIVE *SECURITY PRECAUTIONS* HAVE BEEN TAKEN TO INSURE THAT *NO ONE* MAY ENTER THE CORRIDOR EXCEPT THOSE *ALREADY* PRESENT...

FAMOUS

"AND NOW--YES, YES, THERE IT IS! THERE IS *THE KEY*!!

¿GASP!¿

THAT'S IT! THAT'S IT!!

"OUR LEADER WILL NOW *RAISE* THE KEY FOR ALL TO BEHOLD!"

WHCOSH

I'LL TAKE THAT!

STOP THEM!

I GOT IT, JENNY! LET'S GET OUTTA HERE!

BOON!

DESTROY THEM!

BLAM!

BOON!

WHOOPS! WRONG WAY!

BETTER GO THROUGH THERE!

BUT, ISN'T THAT--?

NO TIME!! C'MON!!

BLAM

WHEW! THAT WAS CLOSE!

DOOR CLIK! CLOSE

..UH... ZOT?

COME ON!

DOOR CLIK! OPEN

WE MADE IT!

21

UH...

NEXT!:

THROUGH THE DOOR!!

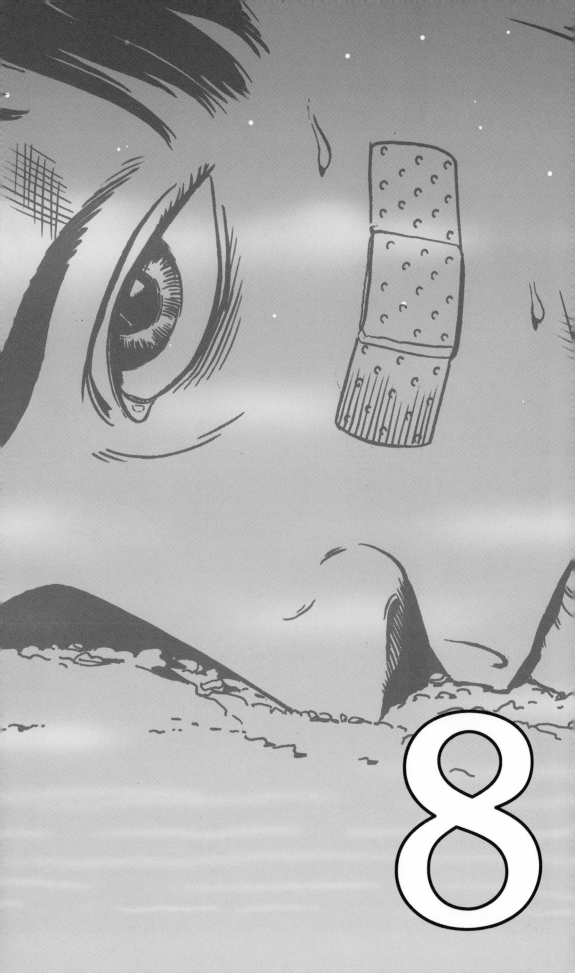

MY FELLOW SIRIANS, THIS IS A *GREAT TRAGEDY!* HEATHEN OUTWORLDERS HAVE STOLEN *THE SACRED KEY* FROM OUR BELOVED *GRAND INQUISITOR!* LET US PRAY THAT OUR *"CHOSEN ONE"* CAN RECOVER THE KEY BEFORE IT IS *TOO LATE!*

I REPEAT, BROTHERS! LET US *PRAY!*

THE CHOSEN ONE'S MEN CANNOT FIRE THEIR WEAPONS FOR FEAR OF PIERCING THE *HUGE TRANSPARENT SPHERE* WHICH SURROUNDS THE DOOR AND MAINTAINS THE *ARTIFICIAL ATMOSPHERE* AROUND IT!

HE MUST USE THE *SACRED JETPACK* TO BRING HIM WITHIN *FIRING RANGE!*

BUT, WHAT IF *THE BOY* IS TRULY *"THE CHOSEN ONE"*?

*NO!* IT'S SOME KIND OF *TRICK!*

AAH, WHO CARES...

*PRAY,* YOU DOGS!!

I DON'T THINK IT *FITS,* JENNY!

STUPID THING *DOESN'T WORK!!*

I DUNNO, ZOT. *SOMETHING'S* HAPPENING...SOME KIND OF *DOOR-FRAME* IS APPEARING!

*WAIT!* MAYBE I--

**CLIK!!**

HA! *GOT IT!*

PREPARE TO *DIE,* SINNERS!!

HEY, IT WON'T OPEN!

WHADDYA *MEAN* "IT WON'T OPEN"??

IT WON'T OPEN! *IT WON'T OPEN!!*

RATTLE RATTLE

4

THAT *BIG* GOON'S GETTING *CLOSER!*

I'M PUSHING AS *HARD* AS I CAN!

"PUSHING"?!

ZOT, THE HINGES ARE ON *THIS SIDE!*

HUH?

PULL, DON'T PUSH!

≋HEH-HEH≋ OF *COURSE...*

*A*ND SO, AT LAST, WITH A *CREAK* AND A *GROAN*--

≋UNNH≋

--THE *WONDROUS ANSWER* TO THE *GREATEST* OF ALL *MYSTERIES*--

*--IS REVEALED!!!*

≋CHOKE≋

...FOR ALL THE WORLDS TO SEE!

NO...

*NO!*

NO!! WE'VE COME *TOO FAR!* I KNOW IT LOOKS HOPELESS, BUT THERE'S GOTTA BE *SOME WAY--*

...

ZOT! LOOK! WE CAN GO *THROUGH* THIS THING! IT'S-- IT'S *NOT SOLID!*

WHAT?!

*WHA-A-AT??!*

THEY'RE *ESCAPING!* I MUST RENEW THE *SACRED PURSUIT!*

*STOP!! THIEVES!!*

THE HEATHENS ARE *PASSING THROUGH* WITH THE KEY IN HAND! CAN OUR *GREAT HERO* CATCH THEM IN TIME?!

IT'S TOO CLOSE TO EVEN *GUESS!*

GO, KIDS, GO!! YOU CAN BEAT 'IM!

HEY! WHAT *ARE* YOU, A *SUBVERSIVE??*

YEAH! QUIET YOU!

IT'S INCREDIBLE! THEY'RE REALLY GONNA *MAKE* IT!

NO!! YOU CAN'T DO THIS TO ME! I AM THE CHOSEN!

I AM THE "GREAT ONE"! I AM--

*SLAM*

*CLIK!*

--LOCKED OUT?!

*RATTLE RATTLE*

I'M LOCKED OUT!!

(7)

≷ỤNNH≷ ...ARE YOU O.K., JEN?

I GUESS SO... *SOME RIDE*, HUH?

WHERE DO YOU THINK WE ARE *NOW*?

SO LONG AS IT STAYS IN ONE PLACE, IT'S FINE BY ME...

HEY, WHAT'RE THESE CLOTHES? AND WHY DO I FEEL SO... SO *TIRED*...?

*AAH! WELCOME, ZACHARY! JENNIFER!* WE'VE BEEN *EXPECTING* YOU. I HOPE YOUR *JOURNEY* THROUGH THE DOOR WASN'T TOO UNSETTLING!

*COME! MASTERS!* THEY'RE *AWAKE!* THEY'RE *AWAKE!*

YOU MUST HAVE MANY *QUESTIONS!*

HA! YOU CAN SAY *THAT* AGAIN! LET'S START WITH *WHERE* WE ARE, WHO *YOU* ARE, AND WHY--

ZOT, *LOOK!* IT'S *THE QUEEN!* BUT SHE'S NOT MOVING... GEEZ, I THINK SHE'S *DEAD!*

MORE *PRECISELY*, JENNIFER, SHE WAS NEVER ACTUALLY ALIVE.

WHAT YOU SEE HERE IS MERELY A *REPLICA* OF THE WOMAN YOU KNOW AS QUEEN OF SIRIUS IV.

10

"REPLICA"? WHAT ARE YOU *TALKING* ABOUT?! WHO ARE YOU?!

YOU DON'T *RECOGNIZE* ME? I'M NOT SURPRISED. THE VILLAINS WHO RULED SIRIUS IV IN YOUR DAY TRIED TO DESTROY ALL RECORDS OF MY REIGN AS *KING GREGORY THE FIRST!* ONLY A FEW SIRUSIANS STILL REMEMBERED HOW I FIRST UNITED THEIR PLANET IN PEACE-- OVER *THREE THOUSAND YEARS BEFORE!*

BUT, LIKE THE QUEEN-- LIKE *ALL* OF US HERE--I'M REALLY JUST A CONSTRUCT...AN *IMITATION* OF THE ORIGINAL...AS ARE *YOU,* MY FRIENDS!

THAT'S *HIM,* ALLRIGHT! "THE *GREAT ZOT"!*

*BAH!* HE'S MUCH TOO *YOUNG!* DOESN'T *DESERVE* TO BE HERE!

OH, *SHH!*

OUTSIDE...

I, UH... STILL DON'T GET IT, YOUR HIGHNESS. WHAT DO YOU MEAN-- *"IMITATION"?*

I DON'T KNOW ABOUT *YOU,* BUT I SURE DON'T *FEEL* LIKE ANYONE BUT ME!

OF COURSE NOT! YOUR BODY HAS BEEN CAREFULLY PREPARED FOR YOU, ZACHARY! ALL IT REQUIRED WAS THAT YOUR SPIRIT BE FREE TO INHABIT IT.

UPON ENTERING THE DOOR, THE SPIRIT WAS TEMPORARILY *RELEASED.* YOU WILL ONLY BE HERE FOR A *SHORT TIME.*

SO WHERE *IS* "HERE"?!

OH, DIDN'T I TELL YOU? GOOD HEAVENS, I'M SORRY! WELL, ≥AHEM≤, HERE GOES:

WELCOME, MY FRIENDS, *TO THE FUTURE!*

WHAT, *AGAIN?!*

...BEG PARDON?

I THINK HE MEANS *SIRIUS IV'S* FUTURE, JENNY...

*CORRECT,* ZACHARY! ...FUNNY, I ALWAYS IMPRESSED THEM WITH THAT LINE *BEFORE...*

*SO,* MY CHILDREN, *COME!* LET ME SHOW YOU THIS FUTURE OF OURS-- --A FUTURE YOU WILL SOON HELP TO *CREATE!*

11

THIS IS AS FAR AS WE CAN *GO*. ONLY IN *THE VALLEY* AND IN THESE *NEARBY HILLS* ARE THE ENERGIES PRESENT TO KEEP OUR SPIRITS FROM FLEEING THEIR NEW BODIES...

THUS, OUR *HOSTS* HAVE PROVIDED US WITH THIS SMALL *"TEMPLE."*

WHO ARE THESE *"HOSTS"?*

WHY, THE PEOPLE OF *SIRIUS IV,* OF COURSE.

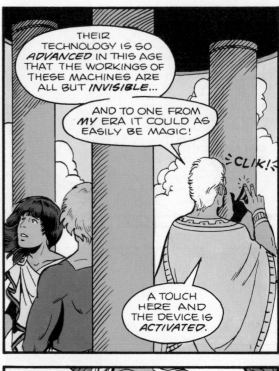

THEIR TECHNOLOGY IS SO *ADVANCED* IN THIS AGE THAT THE WORKINGS OF THESE MACHINES ARE ALL BUT *INVISIBLE*...

AND TO ONE FROM *MY* ERA IT COULD AS EASILY BE MAGIC!

*CLIK!*

A *TOUCH* HERE AND THE DEVICE IS *ACTIVATED.*

OBSERVE NOW THE FUTURE WE *"HEROES"* HELPED MAKE POSSIBLE, SO MANY YEARS AGO...

*VRRRRRMMMM*

AND IN MOMENTS, A NEW LANDSCAPE SEEMS TO TAKE SHAPE AROUND THE TEMPLE...

LOOKS LIKE A BEAUTIFUL CITY, YOUR HIGHNESS, BUT Y'KNOW, EVEN IN *MY* DAY SIRIUS HAD SOME NICE SPOTS...

NOT *THIS* NICE!

*INDEED!* AND TAKE A GOOD LOOK AT WHAT THIS GREAT CITY *DOESN'T* HAVE: THE WALLS!

LONG GONE ARE THE CITY WALLS THAT KEPT OUT THE *"UNWANTED"* IN YOUR TIME! TODAY *ANY* SIRUSIAN CAN WALK DOWN THESE *SPLENDID STREETS!*

12

FINALLY, THIS PLANET IS GUIDED BY THE WILL OF *ALL* ITS CITIZENS! NOT JUST THE GREEDY OR POWER-HUNGRY ONES!

SIRIUS IV HAS BECOME A THRIVING *TRADE CENTER* OF OUR GALAXY!

...AT *PEACE* WITH ITS NEIGHBORS!

THEY'VE EVEN FOUND A WAY TO GET OUR *DAMN WEATHER* UNDER CONTROL! HOW'S *THAT* FOR PARADISE?

NOT BAD... NOT BAD...

AND YOU'RE SAYING JENNY AND I HAD SOMETHING TO DO WITH ALL THIS?

THAT YOU *DID*, OR RATHER YOU *WILL*, SHORTLY AFTER RETURNING FROM THE DOOR!

THAT'S WHY YOU TWO HAVE BEEN HONORED, JUST AS *I* HAVE BEEN... WHEN YOU DIE, YOUR SPIRIT WILL RETURN HERE TO STAY AS LONG AS YOU WISH BEFORE GOING TO YOUR *FINAL REST*.

DO YOU *UNDERSTAND* WHAT I'VE TOLD YOU, ZACHARY? IF YOU DO, THEN THERE IS ONE MORE THING THAT YOU, *ESPECIALLY*, MUST SEE.

I UNDERSTAND IT... YEAH.

THEN COME WITH ME.

*SOON, AT THE FOOT OF THE HILL...*

Y'KNOW, YOU *STILL* HAVEN'T TOLD US HOW THE DOOR *GOT* THERE IN THE *FIRST PLACE* OR HOW ALL THESE...

*PATIENCE*, MY FRIEND... ONE THING AT A TIME...

PLEASE, COME THIS WAY...

GO STRAIGHT AHEAD, ZACHARY.

JENNY, YOU COME WITH ME...

?

*AT FIRST, ZOT'S EYES DO NOT ADJUST TO THE DIM LIGHT...*

13

14

THE TALK LASTS LONG INTO THE AFTERNOON...

WE *HAD* HOPED YOU WOULDN'T HAVE TO *DEAL* WITH 9-JACK-9...

YEAH? WELL, *NOW* I *HOPE* I RUN INTO HIM AGAIN!

'CAUSE WHEN I *DO*, I'M GONNA MAKE HIM *PAY* FOR WHAT HE DID TO YOU! I *SWEAR* I WILL!

OH, HONEY, *DON'T TELL* ME YOU'VE BEEN READING THOSE AWFUL *COMIC-BOOKS* AGAIN...!

NOW, YOU LISTEN TO ME, SON! YOU NEVER HAD A VENGEFUL BONE IN YOUR BODY...AND YOUR MOTHER AND I DON'T EVER WANT THAT TO CHANGE-- NOT FOR *ANYONE*!

I... UNDERSTAND.

BESIDES... *JACK*, IN MANY WAYS, WAS JUST A *TOOL* OF A MAN WHO HAS *ALREADY* BEEN PUNISHED...

...THOUGH... IT SEEMS *STRANGE* NOW TO THINK THAT *WE*, OF ALL PEOPLE, SHOULD'VE BEEN THE ONES TO *OPPOSE* THE KING...

"YOU SEE, UNLIKE YOUR UNCLE MAX--WHO WAS BROUGHT EARLIER--WE DEFECTED FROM SIRIUS IV AS *YOUNG ADULTS*, STILL CARING DEEPLY FOR OUR HOMEWORLD AND ALL OF OUR FRIENDS STILL TRAPPED ON IT...

"IT WAS THROUGH ONE OF THOSE FRIENDS THAT WE FIRST LEARNED OF THE KING'S MALEVOLENT PLANS FOR EARTH...PLANS WHICH ONLY WE WERE IN THE RIGHT POSITION TO STOP...

ZOOM!

"AND TO PROTECT YOU, WE KNEW THE JOB WOULD HAVE TO BE DONE IN COMPLETE SECRECY...

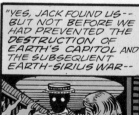

"YES, JACK FOUND US-- BUT NOT BEFORE WE HAD PREVENTED THE DESTRUCTION OF EARTH'S CAPITOL AND THE SUBSEQUENT EARTH-SIRIUS WAR--

SNAP

"--WHICH WOULD HAVE LEFT BOTH SIDES IN NEAR RUINS!"

WE DIDN'T DIE *IN VAIN*, ZACH... I'M SORRY IT TOOK US THIS LONG TO LET YOU KNOW...IT WAS THE ONLY WAY WE COULD THINK OF TO *PROTECT* OUR "LITTLE BOY."

IT *HURT* US TO KEEP IT ALL *HIDDEN* FROM YOU THAT WAY...BUT AT LEAST WE WERE SURE YOU'D KNOW THAT WE'D *ALWAYS* LOVE YOU AND COULD NEVER *DELIBERATELY* DESERT YOU...

I *KNEW*, MOM... I-- I *NEVER* DOUBTED YOU... *NEVER*...

15

HEY, THAT WAS *SOME MEAL!* I'M SURPRISED YOU GUYS HAVEN'T ALL GOTTEN *FAT* LIVING HERE.

THIS IS A *SPECIAL OCCASION,* ZACHARY! YOU AND JENNIFER ARE THE *GUESTS OF HONOR!*

I CAN SEE WHY *ZOT* IS, YOUR HIGHNESS, BUT I STILL DON'T KNOW WHAT *I* DID THAT'S SO SPECIAL...

YOU MUST'VE DONE *SOMETHING,* JE MY PARENTS ALREADY *KNEW* ABOUT

HEY, YEAH!

YOU FOLKS KNOW OUR WHOLE *LIFE-STORIES!* HOW ABOUT ZOT AN' ME?

*L*ATE THAT NIGHT...LONG AFTER THE CITIZENS OF "THE VALLEY" HAVE GONE TO SLEEP...

OH, I *CAN'T* SLEEP NOW... SO MUCH I STILL DON'T UNDERSTAND...

...LIKE WHO *MADE* THE DOOR IN THE *FIRST PLACE.*

HOW DID YOU KNOW WHAT I WAS THINKING?!?

⸗*HA! HA! HA!*⸗ I'M *SMARTER* THAN YOU ARE! NOW, PLEASE, *ONE QUESTION* AT A TIME!

?

YOU ASKED *"WHY"...* WELL...LONG BEFORE YOUR KIND ARRIVED I ALREADY KNEW THE COURSE THEIR HISTORY WOULD TAKE...

...AND I KNEW IF I DIDN'T DO *SOMETHING,* EVEN *I* WOULD HAVE DIED EVENTUALLY...

I ALSO KNEW THESE POOR BEINGS WOULD LOSE *ALL* THEIR HOPE SOONER OR LATER, UNLESS I GAVE 'EM SOMETHING MORE THAN *MYTHS* AND *ANCIENT RELIGIONS...*

WITH MY *PRETTY SHAM* OF A DOOR, I KEPT THAT HOPE ALIVE...

C'MON, WHO *ARE* YOU?

I SAID--

⸗*HA-HA!*⸗ LET ME *FINISH!*

16.

WE DON'T KNOW ANY GIRLS THAT YOUNG HERE IN *THE VALLEY* ZACH...

ARE YOU *SURE* YOU WEREN'T *DREAMING?*

IT DIDN'T *FEEL* LIKE A DREAM.

THIS "GIRL", ZACHARY...

WAS SHE ABOUT 6-8 YEARS OLD...DRESSED IN VIOLET?

THAT'S HER, YOUR HIGHNESS! WHO *IS* SHE? I DIDN'T KNOW SIRIUS IV HAD A *LITTLE GIRL* AS ONE OF IT'S HEROES!

IT *DOESN'T!* THAT GIRL IS MUCH MORE VITAL TO THE PEOPLE OF SIRIUS IV THAN ANY-ONE *HERE* IS! IN FACT YOU SHOULD FEEL *HONORED...*

HOW COME?

THAT "LITTLE GIRL"--

--IS SIRIUS IV.

WELL, *I'LL BE!* YOU NEVER TOLD US SHE APPEARED AS A *LITTLE GIRL*, GREGORY!

YOU NEVER ASKED!

NOW THEN, ZACHARY! ARE YOU READY TO GO? *SEEN ENOUGH*, I HOPE!

READY...YES...

18

BUT HOW **CAN** WE LEAVE, YOUR MAJESTY? WON'T THE DOORWAY BE **HEAVILY GUARDED**?

OH, YOU CAN USE THE **BACK DOOR**.

R-R-RIGHT.

ASK A STUPID QUESTION...

THE BACK DOOR...

THIS PORTAL WILL REMOVE YOUR SPIRITS ONCE MORE SO THAT YOU MAY REJOIN YOUR **OWN** BODIES.

HOW DO YOU KNOW WE WON'T DO THINGS **DIFFERENTLY** NOW THAT WE HAVE ALL THIS **KNOWLEDGE**?

THAT KNOWLEDGE WILL BE... AH... **TAKEN CARE OF**, ZACH.

AND THE KEY?

OH, TAKE IT **BACK**! THE PEOPLE STILL NEED **SOME** MYSTERY...

...KEEPS 'EM IN **SUSPENSE**.

THE LONG GOODBYES FINALLY COME TO A CLOSE...

SO LONG, ZACH... IN **OUR** TIME, WE'LL SEE YOU AGAIN **SOON**...

YEAH, AND FOR ME... A **LIFETIME** FROM NOW... WEIRD...

BUT JUST AS THE YOUNG HEROES ARE ABOUT TO DEPART...

HEY, WHAT'S THAT SOUN--?

...WELL, WHADDYA KNOW...

19

Y'KNOW, I'M FINALLY LEARNING MORE THAN *ONE TUNE* ON THIS THING!

I SURE AM *GLAD* THEY BROUGHT ME... THOUGH I DON'T KNOW JUST *WHY*.

GUESS I DID *SOMETHING* RIGHT, HUH?

I'M SURE YOU *DID*--

--KING *DRUFUS*.

BE *SEEING* YOU...

*CLIK*

*GET* US RETURN NOW, TO THE...*PRESENT-DAY* FUTURE OF, UH...*1965*..? OH, NEVER MIND...

WHERE WE WERE *LAST ISSUE*, HOW'S THAT?

*MAX!* YOUR *GRACE!* GOOD NEWS!

WHAT'S THAT, FATHER KIMM?

THEY'VE *DONE IT.* THEY'VE ENTERED *THE DOOR!*

SOON, ZACHARY AND JENNIFER WILL RETURN TO LEAD US ON OUR *GREAT MISSION!*

?!!

SOONER THAN YOU *THINK*, FATHER KIMM!

*WHOA!* WHAT A *TRIP!*

WELL, *SPEAK OF THE DEVIL!*

WE'RE *ALL EARS*, KIDS. WHAT DID YOU *SEE?*

20

TELL US PLEASE, OH, GREAT ONE! MY *WHOLE LIFE* HAS BEEN SPENT IN *ANTICIPATION* OF THIS MOMENT!

AWW, GET UP FATHER KIMM, *PLEASE!* THIS IS *EMBARRASSING!* WE'LL TELL YOU ALL ABOUT IT! Y'SEE, WE--UH...THAT IS... ...JENNY...?

WELL IT WAS, UH...

...

...

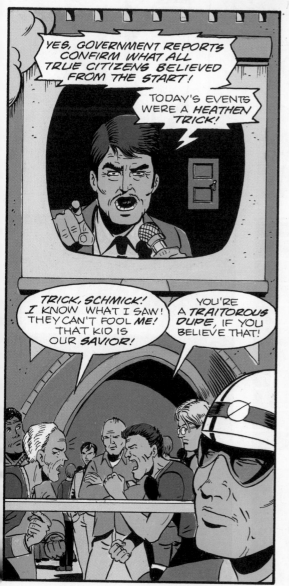

YES, GOVERNMENT REPORTS CONFIRM WHAT ALL *TRUE CITIZENS* BELIEVED FROM THE START!

TODAY'S EVENTS WERE A *HEATHEN TRICK!*

TRICK, SCHMICK! I *KNOW* WHAT I SAW! THEY CAN'T FOOL *ME!* THAT KID IS OUR *SAVIOR!*

YOU'RE A *TRAITOROUS DUPE,* IF YOU BELIEVE THAT!

WHY YOU--!

OOF!

HEY!

*BREAK IT UP!*

[W]HILE AT THE ROYAL PALACE:

KILL HIM! I'LL KILL THAT *WRETCHED BRAT!*

sigh...I WISH YOU *WOULD...*

DAMN! DAMN! DAMN!

WHAT DID THEY *FIND* THERE?

*WHAT?*

*WHAT?*

21

ON THE DENSE EQUATORIAL JUNGLES OF SIRIUS IV, A BIZARRE CULT TORMENTS ITS LATEST VICTIM--BUTCH!

WHADDYA *MEAN*, "SACRED SIMIAN"?!

I DON'T WANNA BE A *MONKEY!* IT WAS ONE OF *YOU* BOZOS THAT TURNED ME INTO ONE IN THE *FIRST PLACE!* *

AS I *ORDERED*, LITTLE *CHIMP!*

OOK! OOK! HA!  OOK! OOK! HA!  AK! AK!  HA! HA!

* WAY BACK IN ISSUE #1.

MY *HOLY SQUADRONS* OF DE-EVOLUTIONARY SOLDIERS HAVE TURNED *MANY* HEATHENS INTO APES, BUT THEY HAVE ALWAYS BEEN CAUGHT AND CAGED BY THE *AUTHORITIES* BEFORE!

TODAY, AT LAST WE HAVE OUR FIRST *TOTAL CONVERT!*

GRRR...

"CONVERT"?? *AAK!* *NO WAY*, FUZZ-BRAIN! YOU AIN'T TURNIN' ME INTO NO *MOONIE!!*

IT IS *FUTILE* TO *RESIST*, MY LITTLE BEASTY! SOON YOU WILL *ACCEPT* US AS *BROTHERS!*

TAKE HIM DOWN, BOYS! IT'S TIME FOR THE SACRED *CEREMONY OF OBEDIENCE!*

2

OUR *SAVIOR* HAS COME! THE *BLUE MONKEY*!!

WE ARE YOUR *SLAVES*, OH GREAT ONE!

YOUR WISH IS OUR *COMMAND*!

...

NOW WE'RE *GETTIN'* SOMEWHERE...

THE *HIGH PRIEST* WILL SEE YOU NOW, GRAND INQUISITOR.

OH, *LUTHOR*, WHY MUST YOU DRAG PRISONERS IN *CHAINS* THIS WAY? IT'S SO *BARBARIC!* AND DON'T TELL ME THIS *PATHETIC LITTLE BOY* IS VIC TAYLOR??

*THE SAME,* HOLINESS! I THOUGHT YOU MIGHT WANT TO *SEE* THE SINNER BEFORE HE IS EXECUTED!

HMM...

I'M NOT SURE I *LIKE* THIS IDEA OF AN *EXECUTION,* MY FRIEND... HOW CAN WE BE CERTAIN THAT VICTOR'S THEFT OF THE KEY WAS NOT PART OF THE *DIVINE PLAN?*

AFTER ALL, HIS FRIEND ZOT *DID* ENTER THE HOLY DOOR, THUS FULFILLING *PROPHECY.*

*NO!* THAT WAS A *HEATHEN TRICK!*

*I* SHOULD HAVE ENTERED THE DOOR, NOT THAT EVIL BRAT *ZOT!*

HEY, DID I SEE...?

I'M SORRY, BUT I HAVE DIFFICULTY THINKING OF THESE CHILDREN AS *"EVIL"...*

...! IT'S *FLOYD!* HE *FOUND* ME!

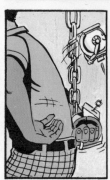

NOW THE *GUN..?*

ATTA-BOY.

6

**BOOM!**

**GUARDS! GUARDS!**

SORRY TO *RUN OUT* ON YOU, GUYS! MAYBE WE CAN HAVE *LUNCH* SOMETIME!

**BLAM!**

ALL RIGHT, LUTHOR, I'M CONVINCED.

FIND HIM... *CAPTURE* HIM...

AND *KILL* HIM...

*STOP THAT BOY!*

HEY, *WATCH OUT!*

HURRY, MEN! DON'T LOSE HIM IN THE CROWD!

C'MON, FLOYD! YOU'VE GOTTA HELP ME FIND ZOT AND THE OTHER'S *FAST!*

I DUNNO, VIC! ARE YOU SURE YOU NEED THE *HELP?*

HUH?

7

VIC, YOU REMEMBER *JENNY WEAVER*, DON'T Y-- HUH?!

*PEABODY!* YOU'RE *HERE!* YOU'RE *O.K.!!*

EVIDENTLY, YES, ZACHARY.

HE GOT HERE JUST A *MINUTE AGO!*

I GUESS THOSE *SHOTS* HE TOOK WEREN'T AS BAD AS I *TOLD* YOU, THOUGH I COULD'VE *SWORN*--

ZACHARY, I SUGGEST WE DEPART *QUICKLY.* I DETECT *APPROACHING POLICE CRAFT.*

YEAH, BUT HOW'RE WE SUPPOSED TO GET *DOWN* FROM HERE??

MAX? *COME IN,* MAX. DO YOU *READ* ME?

I READ YOU, ZACH!

THE GANG'S ALL HERE -- *PLUS ONE!*

ON MY WAY!

*FNOOSH*

WHOA!

HOP IN, KIDS! THE METER'S RUNNING!

9

ON THE ROYAL PALACE, THE CONSPIRACY IS MEETING...

GENTLEMEN,

HELLO, *VON CLOKMANN.*

I ASSUME YOUR *LITTLE CHARADE* WITH THE *HIGH PRIEST* WENT WELL! THE BOY HAS ALREADY MET WITH HIS PARTNERS.

THEY'RE APPROACHING THE DOCKS BY LAND, TRYING TO REMAIN *INCONSPICUOUS.* THE FOOLS DON'T KNOW THAT I COULD HAVE HAD THEM DESTROYED *AN HOUR AGO* IF I'D WANTED.

OH, YES, AND *ZOT* IS WITH THEM.

THEN HE'S *BACK!* SOMEHOW, THE WRETCHED EARTHLING IS BACK FROM THE DOOR! I *MUST* KNOW WHAT HE FOUND THERE! I *MUST!*

*SO,* GENTLEMEN, HOW IS OUR *BUNGLING COLLEAGUE,* TWIK, COMING ALONG?

⇒HEE⇒ ⇒HEE⇒

I WOULDN'T LAUGH *TOO* HARD IF I WERE YOU, SWIMBLER!

YOU MAY BE IN *HOTTER WATERS SOON* IF YOU CAN'T PAY YOUR SHARE OF *9-JACK-9'S FEE!*

10

TWIK STILL HAS SOME *LIFE* IN HIM, AFTER ALL -- EVEN THOUGH HIS MIND IS ALL BUT *OBLITERATED* AT THIS POINT.

SPEAKING OF WHICH, I'D SAY OUR GADGET HAS PLOWED THROUGH ENOUGH OF TWIK'S BRAIN. TURN IT OFF NOW.

OH, *PLEASE*, SHRAPP! LET'S--

*NOW*, I SAID!

I ENJOY WATCHING IT AS MUCH AS *YOU* DO, BUT WE HAVEN'T THE *TIME* FOR IT. WE'VE GOT TO GET TO THE ISLAND AND INTERCEPT--

*NO!*

NO, I WANT TO GO THERE *ALONE*, GENERAL! I HAVE A *PERSONAL INTEREST* IN THESE HEATHENS!

ZOT AND THAT *LITTLE WENCH* OF HIS HAVE BEEN *BEYOND THE DOOR** AND *RETURNED* -- STEALING MY CHANCE TO LEARN ITS *SECRET*. BUT WITH THE TRAP WE'VE LAID I CAN FINALLY STEAL IT BACK!

AND ONCE I HAVE, I SHALL *RIP* THEIR LITTLE LIMBS OFF, *ONE BY ONE*, AND GRIND THEM TO *PASTE* BENEATH MY HEEL!

*LAST ISSUE.

GOOD DAY, GENTLEMEN.

Y'KNOW, I LIKE HIS ATTITUDE!

11

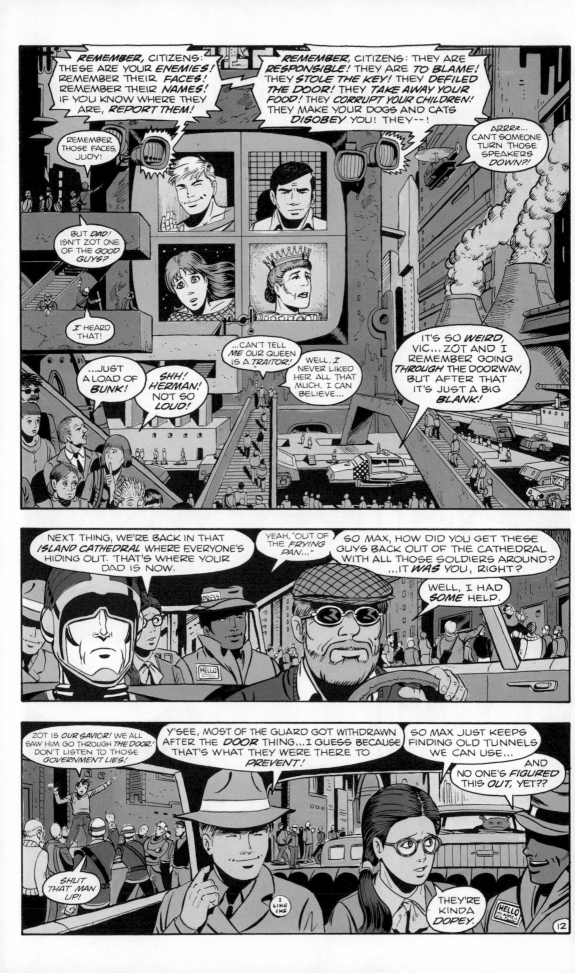

HAVE YOU HEARD *THE LATEST*?! ZOT IS *BACK FROM THE DOOR!* WE'RE ALL MEETING AT THE OLD *CHURCH OF THE KEY* TONIGHT TO *CELEBRATE!*

?

*GREAT!* COUNT ME *IN!*

SAME *HERE!*

*HEY!* YOU KNOW THERE'S A LAW AGAINST THAT KIND OF MEETING!

AW, *TAKE A HIKE!*

*YEAH,* YOU HEARD HER! WE'VE HAD ENOUGH OF YOU *"LAW 'N' ORDER"* JERKS PUSHING US AROUND! IF YOU DON'T *WATCH YOUR STEP* --

*CLK!*

÷Gasp!÷ YOU...YOU WOULDN'T *DARE* --

PUT THAT *KNIFE DOWN!* YOU'RE *UNDER ARREST!*

I LIKE IKE

YOU WANNA ARREST US *ALL,* COP? *GO AHEAD!*

THIS ISN'T RIGHT, JENNY.

*I'LL* SAY IT ISN'T! *"ZOT"* THIS, *"ZOT"* THAT...

HEY, *I* WENT THROUGH THE DOOR, *TOO,* DOES ANYBODY *NOTICE?*

*SOME HOURS LATER, UNDERNEATH THE ISLAND CATHEDRAL OF SHOTARO...*

OUR ROBOT *PEABODY* WILL BE WITH US IN A *MINUTE,* FATHER KIMM. I KNOW YOU'RE NOT SUPPOSED TO LET *MACHINES* IN HERE...

YOUR WILL IS *OURS,* GREAT ZOT! BUT AREN'T YOU AFRAID THAT 9-JACK-9 MIGHT *POSSESS* YOUR ROBOT?

NOT IF JACK CAN'T *GET IN* TO DO IT. WE'LL BE SAFE ENOUGH.

*DAD...* I WAS *SO* SCARED YOU'D BE MAD AT ME!

MORE LIKE *"FURIOUS",* SON! YOUR MOTHER AND I HAVE BEEN WORRIED *SICK!*

BUT, RIGHT NOW, WE'RE JUST GLAD YOU'RE *ALIVE!*

THAT'S *HIM,* YOUR GRACE...

13

I WISH YOU'D KNOCK OFF THIS *"GREAT ZOT"* STUFF, FATHER KIMM...IT'S GIVING ME THE CREEPS!

AS YOU WISH, *YOUR HOLINESS!*

BETTER QUIT WHILE YOU'RE *AHEAD*, ZACH!

YOU'RE *RIGHT*... I SHOULD HAVE TOLD YOU AND MOM, BUT... BUT...

I KNOW -- WE "WOULDN'T UNDERSTAND"-- WELL...MAYBE YOU WERE RIGHT...

PARDON ME, CHILD... BUT IS IT TRUE THAT YOU WERE PRESENT WHEN MY SON...*DIED?*

VIC, THIS IS THE *QUEEN OF SIRIUS IV.* SHE'S JOINED IN OUR STRUGGLE AGAINST THE *CONSPIRACY!*

OH, *YOUR MAJESTY,* I--

BLAM!

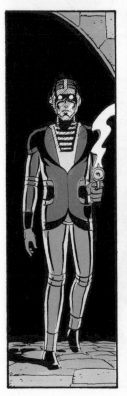

JACK.

DROP *THE GUN,* ZACHARY.

14

WELL, SINNERS! NOW THAT MR. 9 HAS BROUGHT YOU *ALL TOGETHER* AND ALLOWED OUR NEEDED *"PEACEFUL ENTRY,"* I BELIEVE THE TIME HAS COME FOR YOU TO *PAY FOR YOUR CRIMES!*

YOU, THIEF, WILL *NOT PERISH* FROM YOUR WOUND. I REQUESTED THAT YOU BE *ALIVE* FOR THIS...

SCREW YOU-- =UNNH!= --YOU *MANIAC!* YOU WON'T GET AWAY WITH THIS!

DON'T TRY TO *MOVE*, VIC!

YOU THINK YOU CAN *ESCAPE*, BOY? *HOW??* WHERE'S YOUR *"GREAT HERO"* NOW? NOT THESE TWO WHELPS BEHIND ME, THEY'RE AS HELPLESS AS YOU ARE!

GOTTA GET THESE ROPES LOOSE... TRY AND GRAB JACK'S GUN...

AND WHEN THEY'VE TOLD ME WHAT I WANT TO KNOW, THEY'LL DIE JUST AS SURELY AS YOU! YOU'LL NOTICE THAT THE ROPES THAT BIND YOU HAVE BEEN SOAKED IN THE SAME *FLAMMABLE LIQUID* USED IN THIS SHRINE'S *CEREMONY OF TORCHES* --

WE KNOW WHAT YOU PLAN TO DO, *VON CLOKMANN.* WE'RE NOT AFRAID. THE *SPIRIT OF THE KEY* WILL PROTECT US!

SURE...

SILENCE, PRIEST! THE SPIRIT STANDS AT *MY SIDE NOW!*

HEATHENS--

PREPARE TO--

REVERT!

?

15

~AAR!!~
AK! AK! OOK!
~OOKA!!~
**GRAA!!**

YOU DIDN'T PAY ME FOR *THAT*, VON CLOKMANN. I'VE ALREADY *FULFILLED* MY OBLIGATIONS.

I DON'T DO BUSINESS WITH *LOSERS*, MISTER INQUISITOR. I'VE HAD QUITE ENOUGH OF YOU AND YOUR *CONSPIRACY*. AFTER I LEAVE, YOU WON'T BE SEEING ME AGAIN.

THAT IS... IF YOU'RE *LUCKY!*

ON...
R...HA-HA!

TIE 'EM *GOOD 'N' TIGHT*, BOYS!

HEY BUTCH, YOU BETTER *DITCH THAT CIGAR* BEFORE WE GET *HOME!*

MOM'D *KILL YOU* IF SHE FOUND OUT!

WELL, ZACHARY, I HOPE YOU'VE ENJOYED THIS HALF AS MUCH AS *I HAVE!*

HUH?

*UNNH...*

WE BETTER GET HIM TO A BED!

*DID* KILL YOUR PARENTS, YOU KNOW. THAT *WASN'T* [M]E. OF COURSE, IT WAS JUST *ANOTHER JOB* TO ME...I [K]OW THAT'S NOT LIKELY TO MAKE YOU ANY MORE FORGIVING...

YOU WERE JUST A TOOL OF THE KING. I KNOW THAT NOW.

YOU KNOW, TOO, THAT SOMEDAY... I *WILL* KILL YOU.

*COULD BE.*

BUT IF YOU DO, YOU CAN BET I'LL TAKE YOU *WITH* ME!

YOU'LL TRY...

...BE *SEEING* YOU.

PING

IS VIC--?

HE'LL MAKE IT, ZACH. HE JUST NEEDS SOME REST...

...I... REALLY THOUGHT I WAS *SAFE*...

*SOON...*

CLIK! *WHRRRR!* UK~KK...GOH--G-- *GOOD HEAVENS.*

HEY, *LOOK!* THE EGGHEAD GOT *ROBBIE* WORKING AGAIN!

HEY, *CHROME-DOME!* GUESS WHO?

DON'T BE TOO ROUGH ON HIM, BUTCH!

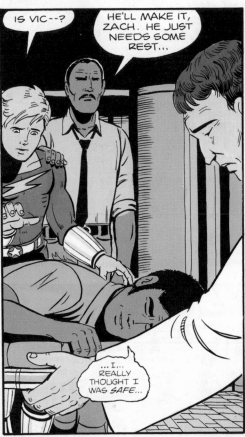

*SO, BLONDIE*-- WE GOT SOME *UNFINISHED BUSINESS,* OR WHAT?

NOT FOR *LONG,* BUTCH. *NOT FOR LONG!*

THAT NIGHT...

SO IT'S JUST *US* NOW, EH, GENERAL?

WELL, *NEVER MIND!* WE'LL MAKE A *DANDY TEAM,* YOU AND I! I NEVER LIKED THOSE OTHER TWO, ANYWAY...

*SO!* WHO IS IT YOU WANTED ME TO MEET?

OH, JUST SOMEBODY WHO CLAIMS YOU *OWE* HIM SOMETHING.

ODD, I DON'T REMEMBER ANY--

HELLO, WEAVIS...

*SHRAPP, WAIT! NO!!* I CAN'T PAY HIM YET!!

CLIK

*SHRAPP, PLEASE!!*

*DON'T L--*

SLAM

ON AN ISLAND CATHEDRAL, ON A DISTANT WORLD, IN ANOTHER UNIVERSE...

WE SHOULD GET MOVING **SOON**, VIC...

HEY, AS LONG AS I CAN'T GO **WITH** YOU, ZACH, I'D LIKE TO SEND **FLOYD** ALONG TO HELP.

THAT IS, IF YOU THINK YOU CAN **USE** HIM.

YOU KIDDING? **OF COURSE** WE CAN! BUT ARE YOU SURE YOU WANT TO **ENTRUST** HIM TO ME?

YEAH... DESIGNER SAID HE WAS **FOOL-PROOF.**

OUGHTTA APPLY...

VICTOR, YOU'VE DONE A GREAT SERVICE TO OUR PLANET...

...BUT **MORE** THAN THAT, YOU WERE A FRIEND TO MY SON, THE PRINCE, WHEN HE MOST **NEEDED** ONE.

I'D LIKE TO THINK THAT HIS LAST HOURS WERE **EASIER** BECAUSE OF THAT...

YEAH, NO THANKS TO **YOU**, "YOUR **MAJESTY**"...

WHAT??

OH, I'VE BEEN **THINKING** ABOUT YOU -- ABOUT WHAT DRUFUS TOLD ME.

HE SAID YOU HARDLY EVER **NOTICED** HIM! SO DON'T -- *UNNH!* DON'T MAKE LIKE YOU -- *OWW!*

VIC, **STOP** IT!

**VICTOR,** YOU'LL **AGGRAVATE** THAT **WOUND!** PLEASE LAY STILL -- AND ON YOUR **STOMACH** LIKE I **TOLD** YOU!

THAT WAS **OUT OF LINE,** VIC! YOU'D BETTER APOLOGIZE!

THAT WON'T BE **NECESSARY,** MR. TAYLOR. YOUR SON COULDN'T POSSIBLY KNOW WHAT IT WAS LIKE FOR ME!

I TRIED TO GUIDE THAT CHILD AS BEST I COULD, BUT AS QUEEN I HAVE SO **MANY...**

...**HAD**...SO MANY DUTIES TO PERFORM.

2

WELL, I'M SORRY YOU'RE OUT OF A JOB, YOUR HIGHNESS, BUT Y'KNOW, I CAN THINK OF ONE KID WHO WOULD'VE SAID YOU WERE BETTER OFF THIS WAY...

'CAUSE THAT'S ALL DRUFUS EVER WANTED WAS A LITTLE TIME TO BE HIMSELF FOR A CHANGE--

--BUT THE KING AND THAT... UNCLE WHAT'S-HIS-NAME ALWAYS EXPECTED HIM TO BE LITTLE MISTER PERFECT ALL THE TIME...

SUCH A LOUSY WASTE...

DON'T DESPAIR, VICTOR. HIS LIFE ON SIRIUS IV MAY BE DONE--

--BUT THE PRINCE'S SOUL STILL LIVES BEYOND THE DOOR.

THE HELL IT DOES! ZACH AND JENNY DIDN'T SEE HIM THERE, DID THEY?

WE MIGHT HAVE!

YEAH, THAT WHOLE TRIP'S JUST A BLANK NOW, REMEMBER? WHO KNOWS WHAT WE SAW BEYOND THE DOOR?

HA! YOU'VE BEEN AROUND OLD LEMON-HEAD TOO LONG, JENNY...

OH, IT'S NOT THAT, IT'S JUST-- I DUNNO--JUST A FEELING I'VE GOT... I MEAN, SOMETHING DID HAPPEN THERE, EVEN IF--

FATHER KIMM! NEWS!

3

THAT'S O.K., NEITHER DO *THEY!* THEY JUST *ACT* LIKE THEY DO!

C'MON, *GET SERIOUS!* GIVE IT A TRY!

Uh... ALL RIGHT.

HA! HA! HA! HA!

I CAN'T DO IT!

HOPELESS...

HEY, *PEABODY! YOU'VE* GOT THE FACE TO BE A *SUPERHERO!* HOW ABOUT IT?

NO, THANK YOU. I WAS NOT PROGRAMMED TO BE *PSYCHOPATHIC...*

BUTCH IS RIGHT ABOUT *ONE THING,* MAX... A *GUN* AND *BOOT-JETS* AREN'T GONNA STOP *AN ARMY!*

THEN WE HAVE TO MAKE SURE THAT THAT ARMY DOESN'T GET *CALLED UP,* ZACH!

HEY, REMEMBER, MAX, FLOYD CAN RECORD WHAT HE SEES AND REPLAY IT!

SON, DON'T *BOTHER* THE MAN, HE'S--

*HOLD ON,* RAYMOND...THIS COULD BE USEFUL...

TELL ME, VIC: I'VE SEEN FLOYD'S *REPLAY* CAPABILITY, BUT CAN HE DIGITIZE A *SCENE* FOR *LIVE TRANSMISSION?*

*SURE!* IF YOU'VE GOT A *RECEIVER.*

RIGHT. HMM...

?

TAP TAP

WELL, DON'T KEEP US IN *SUSPENSE,* MAX! WHAT'S MY *BATTLE-PLAN?*

MAKE THAT *OUR* "BATTLE-PLAN," ZACH!

NOW, LISTEN CAREFULLY...

5

WAIT! LET'S GO BACK A MINUTE OR TWO:

CITIZENS! THE TIME HAS COME!

EARTHLING HEATHEN KILLED YOUR KING AND KILLED HIS SON! THEY HAVE DEFILED YOUR MOST HOLY TEMPLE AND EVEN THE SACRED DOORWAY AT THE EDGE OF THE UNIVERSE!!

OUR RESPONSE IS CLEAR: HOLY WAR ON EARTH MUST BE OUR ANSWER!

UNDER SIRIAN LAW AND AS PERMITTED BY THE HIGH PRIEST, YOU ARE NOW UNDER MY DIRECT COMMAND!

NO! WE FOLLOW ONLY ZOT! NOT YOU!

YEAH, WHAT HE SAID!

TRAITORS...

SILENCE!

OH, I WISH I WAS HOME AND IN BED!

ANY DISSENT WILL BE PUNISHABLE BY DEATH!

HMM...

GOT THAT, CITIZENS?

...

HENCEFORTH, THE VERY MENTION OF THE NAME "ZOT" SHALL BE CONSIDERED AN ACT OF HIGH TREASON!

I AM YOUR SOLE AND RIGHTFUL LEADER!

8

MEANWHILE, IN THE CONTROL-ROOM, NEARBY...

HEY! YOU'RE NOT ALLOWED IN H--

OOK! OOK!

CHARGE!

REVERT!

REVERT!

BA SH!

REVERT! PRAISE THE BLUE MONKEY!!

OOK! OOK!

REVERT!

GAAH!

ALL YOUR'S, DOC! DO YOUR STUFF!

MY PLEASURE, BUTCH!

REVERT!

GEEKKH!

AK! AK!

THINK YOU CAN MAKE IT WORK FOR US, MAX?

HA! PIECE O' CAKE!

AND BACK IN THE STUDIO...

--THAT ALL DESTROYERS WILL CONVERGE AT THE FOLLOWI--

??

SORRY TO INTERRUPT THE PROGRAM, GENERAL--

--BUT I'LL BET YOUR RATINGS ARE ABOUT TO SHOOT THROUGH THE ROOF!

GUARDS! DESTROY HIM!

ZAF!

9

GUESS AGAIN, DOG FACE!

ZOT'S STILL *IN DANGER*, MAX! I'M GOING UP TO *HELP HIM!*

*--BUT, IF HE IS THE CHOSEN ONE, THE SPIRIT OF THE KEY WILL WIN FOR HIM!*

AND IN OVER A BILLION HOMES...

THEN ZOT *REALLY IS* THE "CHOSEN ONE"?

NO!

*NEARBY...* YOUR HOLINESS, DID YOU *HEAR--*?!

CARE TO *STRIKE A DEAL,* BOY?

GETTING *NERVOUS,* HUH?

I HEARD! I *HEARD!*

DON'T BE A *FOOL,* BOY! THESE SHEEP *WANT* TO BE LED! IT'S SO *CONFUSING,* BUT--

THEY ONLY WANT TO *RULE THEMSELVES!* YOU NEVER LET THEM!

THEY NEVER *TRIED,* YOU NAIVE BRAT! AND THEY *NEVER WILL!* DESTROY *ME* AND THEY'LL GET ANOTHER "TYRANT" JUST AS CRUEL, *OR WORSE!*

FORGET IT, SHRAPP! I'M NOT *BUYING!*

IT'S *THE TRUTH,* BOY! YOUR "BELOVED *CITIZENS*" WOULD SPIT THEIR *FREEDOM* RIGHT BACK IN YOUR *FACE!*

*SAYS YOU,* SHRAPP!!

I'M SORRY, JENNY, DID YOU *SAY* SOMETHING? ...JENNY?

WHERE DID SHE GET TO?

THAT'S THE LAST OF YOUR ROBOTS, SHRAPP!

11

12

UNNH!

SHRAPP...

YOU... VILLAIN, YOU.

13

14

OH, ZOT! I WAS *SO SCARED*. I THOUGHT YOU--

OH, BUT YOU'RE *O.K.!* AND YOU WON! *YOU WON!*

÷*OOF!*÷ YEAH, I--

÷*HA! HA!*÷

I GUESS I *DID!*

SO HOW D'YA *FEEL*, HERO?

UH... KINDA *NAUSEOUS*, ACTUALLY...

*GREAT ONE! FORGIVE ME!*

?

?

OH NO! NOT *ANOTHER ONE!!* IS EVERYONE ON THIS PLANET *CRAZY?!*

*THEY* ARE IF HE IS, ZACH! THAT'S THE *HIGH PRIEST!*

WE ARE *YOURS* TO COMMAND, OH, GREAT ONE! OH PLEASE *FORGIVE US!* WE ONLY DID WHAT WE THOUGHT WAS RIGHT, OH, PLEASE DON'T...

I SHOULD *WARN* YOU, KID, THEY WERE ALREADY *KNEELING IN THE STREETS* WHEN WE RUSHED IN HERE...

APPARENTLY, THEY WERE READY TO WORSHIP WHOEVER CAME OUT ON TOP.

BUT MAX, YOU MEAN THEY ALL--?

THIS *WHOLE WORLD* THINKS I'M THEIR--?

...

15

I'M SO SORRY...

WELL, WHAT DID YOU THINK BEING A "HERO" IS ALL ABOUT?!

DIDN'T--?

DIDN'T YOU *HEAR* WHAT HE SAID?

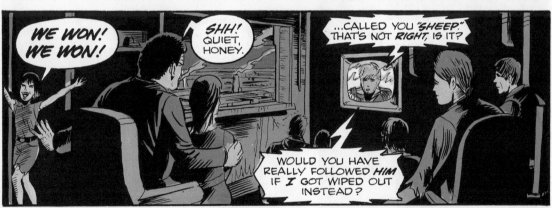

WE WON! WE WON!

SHH! QUIET, HONEY.

...CALLED YOU "SHEEP." THAT'S NOT *RIGHT*, IS IT?

WOULD YOU HAVE REALLY FOLLOWED *HIM* IF *I* GOT WIPED OUT INSTEAD?

MAYBE I'M *DUMB*, BUT ISN'T JUSTICE MORE THAN JUST A...

...A *PUNCH* IN THE *MOUTH*??

19

WHAT CAN I *TELL* YOU GUYS...? HOW CAN I LEAD YOU TO WHERE YOU WON'T BE...*LED?*

LOOK AT ME. I'M A KID. WHAT DO I *KNOW* ABOUT YOU? ABOUT WHAT YOU *NEED?*

ALL I WANTED TO DO WAS HELP YOU GET PAST ALL THE *LIES*...

THAT *DOESN'T* MEAN I'VE GOT ALL THE ANSWERS...

IT'S NOT THAT I DON'T *WANT* TO HELP YOU...I *DO.*

BUT I'M ONLY A HERO...

C-LIK

??

YOU'VE GOT TO LEARN TO...

...TO LIVE... WITHOUT...

...

ZOT!

20

SOON... JUST SIMPLE *EXHAUSTION*, MY LADY. I'M SURE THE *SPIRIT OF THE KEY* WILL--

OH, *ENOUGH ALREADY!*

HEY, *DOC!* MY *FORCE-FIELD* JUST *BLINKED OUT!*

COME! WE MUST JOIN THE *BLUE MONKEY!*

REVERT! REVERT!

REVERT! REVERT!

HI-HO! HI-HO!

SHUT UP!

OH, THE BATTERY ONLY LASTS A *FEW DAYS*, BUTCH. I CAN GET YOU A *RECHARGE*, LATER.

BUT IF THOSE *"DEVO"* GUYS SEE ME LIKE *THIS*--

-¡ *Gasp!* ¡-

RUN! RUN! OUR LEADER IS *STRIPPED OF HIS POWER!*

HUH? NO, WAIT! *WAIT!* COME BACK!

EASY COME, EASY GO...

*M*ORNING...

BUT YOU *MUST RETURN*, ZACHARY! SIRIUS IV *NEEDS* YOU!

LIKE A *HOLE IN THE HEAD*, FATHER KIMM!

WHAT YOU GUYS *REALLY* NEED IS TO *THINK FOR YOURSELVES!*

THAT *MAY BE*, YOUNG MAN--

--BUT IF YOU LEAVE US FOR GOOD, THERE WILL BE *ANARCHY!* WHAT DIFFERENCE WILL OUR *NEW WISDOM* MAKE THEN?

AT LEAST *RETURN* TO GIVE US *GUIDANCE!*

WOULD IT REALLY MATTER *THAT MUCH*, MAX?

IT *COULD.*

21

YOU SAY ALL I GOTTA DO IS STEP THROUGH AND I'LL BE *HUMAN* AGAIN?

"AGAIN"?

IF MY THEORY IS CORRECT, YES! MIND YOU, I'M BASING MY CONCLUSIONS ON SOME *EXCEPTIONALLY*--

YEAH, YEAH. *WHATEVER.*

I'LL JOIN YOU IN A SEC, BUTCH...

OKAY, SIS...

*GERONIMO!*

*AAG!!*

WHOOPS!

SORRY...

DO YOU FEEL *ALRIGHT,* THOUGH?

BORN TO RULE

-GRRRR-

YEAH, I'M FINE...

FA-A-A-ASCINATING...

Uh... I'M NOT SURE I *GET* IT, MAX...

NEITHER AM I, JENNY...

NOT...*YET.*

WELL, I GUESS THIS IS *GOODBYE...*

YOU'RE REALLY GONNA TRY AND SET THAT WHOLE PLANET RIGHT, EVEN AFTER YOU TOLD 'EM TO *TAKE A HIKE?* YOU'RE TALKING ABOUT *BILLIONS OF PEOPLE,* ZOT!

HOW CAN YOU REALLY *HELP THEM* WITHOUT *LEADING THEM* LIKE YOU SAID?

IT'LL BE HARD...

Y'KNOW, IT'S *PROBABLY IMPOSSIBLE...*

*PROBABLY* YEAH...

BUT, YOU *STILL* THINK YOU CAN DO IT...?

23

For my Father

who never told me
what "can't be done"

and whose whole life
was a work of art.

THE END